WeightWatchers® momentum™ Cookbook

200 Easy Recipes to Get—and *Keep*—You Going

About Weight Watchers

Weight Watchers International, Inc. is the world's leading provider of weight management services, operating globally through a network of Company-owned and franchise operations. Weight Watchers holds over 48,000 weekly meetings, where members receive group support and education about healthful eating patterns, behavior modification, and physical activity. Weight-loss and weight-management results vary by individual. We recommend that you attend Weight Watchers meetings to benefit from the supportive environment you'll find there and follow the comprehensive Weight Watchers program, which includes food plans, an activity plan, and a thinking-skills plan. In addition, Weight Watchers offers a wide range of products, publications and programs for those interested in weight loss and weight control. For the Weight Watchers meeting nearest you, call 800-651-6000. For information on bringing Weight Watchers to your workplace, call **800-8AT-WORK**. Also, visit us at our Web site, **WeightWatchers.com**, or look for ***Weight Watchers Magazine*** at your newsstand or in your meeting room.

SLICED STEAK WITH CRISPY POLENTA, PAGE 181

WEIGHT WATCHERS PUBLISHING GROUP

EDITORIAL DIRECTOR	**NANCY GAGLIARDI**
CREATIVE DIRECTOR	**ED MELNITSKY**
PRODUCTION MANAGER	**ALAN BIEDERMAN**
PHOTO EDITOR	**DEBORAH HARDT**
EDITORIAL ASSISTANT	**CELIA SHATZMAN**
FOOD EDITOR	**EILEEN RUNYAN**
EDITOR	**DEBORAH MINTCHEFF**
NUTRITION CONSULTANT	**U.BEATE KRINKE**
PHOTOGRAPHER	**RITA MAAS**
PHOTO STYLIST	**ANNE DISRUDE**
PROP STYLIST	**CATHY COOK**
ART DIRECTOR	**DANIELA HRITCU**

ON THE COVER: Stir-Fried Beef and Asparagus, page 184

SKU #11170 Printed in the USA

About Our Recipes

We make every effort to ensure that you will have success with our recipes.

For best results and for nutritional accuracy, please keep these guidelines in mind:

- Recipes in this book have been developed for members who are following the Weight Watchers® Momentum™ plan. We include ***POINTS*** ® values for every recipe. ***POINTS*** values are assigned based on calories, fat (grams), and fiber (grams) provided for a serving size of a recipe.

- All recipes feature approximate nutritional information; our recipes are analyzed for Calories (Cal), Total Fat (Fat), Saturated Fat (Sat Fat), Trans Fat (Trans Fat), Cholesterol (Chol), Sodium (Sod), Carbohydrates (Carb), Dietary Fiber (Fib), Protein (Prot), and Calcium (Calc).

- Nutritional information for recipes that include meat, poultry, and fish are based on cooked skinless boneless portions (unless otherwise stated), with the fat trimmed.

- We recommend that you buy lean meat and poultry, then trim it of all visible fat before cooking. When poultry is cooked with the skin on, we suggest removing the skin before eating.

- Before serving, divide foods—including any vegetables, sauce, or accompaniments—into portions of equal size according to the designated number of servings per recipe.

- Any substitutions made to the ingredients will alter the "Per serving" nutritional information and may affect the ***POINTS*** value.

- All fresh fruits, vegetables, and greens in recipes should be rinsed before using.

- All ™ Filling Extra suggestions have a ***POINTS*** value of ***0*** unless otherwise stated.

- Read about the Simply Filling technique in Book 6: Keep on Tracking.

TURKEY WRAPS WITH LEMON-YOGURT SAUCE, PAGE 46

contents

PASTA SALAD WITH
APPLE AND CHICKEN,
PAGE 72

Introduction

Start the New Year right with Weight Watchers® *Momentum*™ *Cookbook*. It will be easy to eat wisely, watch your portions, *and* feel satisfied at every meal with our quick-to-make, delicious dishes.

Inside, you'll find 200 of our tastiest recipes geared toward your busy lifestyle, including:

- **breakfasts that will help you start your day right**
- **pack-and-go soup-and-sandwich lunches**
- **no-cook or just-a-zap-in-the-microwave suppers**
- **hearty dishes for the times when you feel *really* hungry**
- **no-fuss suppers that make it a breeze to feed your whole family**
- **a dessert cart to satisfy your sweet tooth**

Plus:

- **super-quick snacks for the times when you need a nosh in a hurry**

What's new about this cookbook is the addition of even more of those healthful legumes, such as peas, beans, and lentils, as well as those good-for-you whole grains, such as brown rice, wild rice, whole wheat, buckwheat, barley, bulgur, cornmeal, and quinoa. The good news is that not only are whole grains rich in flavor and nutrients but they also leave you feeling satisfied longer than their processed counterparts. And, as always, we've developed recipes that keep the fat and sodium low, use lean meats, poultry, and fish, and include a wide variety of fresh fruits and vegetables.

As a bonus, we've included two new tips throughout the pages: Filling Extra is all about ways to incorporate additional fresh fruits and vegetables and whole grains into the recipes for even smarter eating. **In the Kitchen** offers savvy advice about preparing the recipes and choosing ingredients.

We hope you'll be as excited about our *Momentum Cookbook* as we are. Our goal, as always, is to offer everyday recipes that make it easy for you to stay on track and maintain your motivation while enjoying every bite. Good luck and happy eating!

chapter 1

beyond my usual breakfast

Start your morning right with these delicious meals

Corn and Green Chile Frittata

PREP 10 MIN | **COOK** 15 MIN | **SERVES** 4

- **6 large eggs**
- **1 cup frozen corn kernels, thawed**
- **1 (4½-ounce) can chopped mild green chiles, drained**
- **¼ cup fat-free milk**
- **2 teaspoons chopped fresh thyme or ½ teaspoon dried**
- **½ teaspoon salt**
- **¼ teaspoon black pepper**
- **3 dashes hot pepper sauce**
- **12 cherry tomatoes, halved**

1 Whisk together the eggs, corn, chiles, milk, thyme, salt, black pepper, and pepper sauce in a large bowl.

2 Spray a medium nonstick skillet with nonstick spray and set over medium heat. Add the egg mixture and sprinkle with the tomatoes. Cover and cook until the eggs are set, about 15 minutes. Cut the frittata into 4 wedges. Serve hot, warm, or at room temperature.

PER SERVING (1 wedge): 168 Cal, 8 g Fat, 3 g Sat Fat, 0 g Trans Fat, 318 mg Chol, 493 mg Sod, 12 g Carb, 2 g Fib, 12 g Prot, 74 mg Calc. *POINTS* value: *4.*

In the Kitchen

The green chiles you'll find in squat little cans in the Mexican aisle of your supermarket are extremely mild, as they are usually seedless Anaheim peppers. If you prefer a little more spice with your eggs, substitute a jalapeño or two—fresh or canned—for the green chiles.

This recipe works with the Simply Filling technique.

CORN AND GREEN
CHILE FRITTATA

PROVENÇAL OMELETTE

Provençal Omelette

PREP 5 MIN | **COOK** 5 MIN | **SERVES** 2

- **2 large eggs**
- **2 large egg whites**
- **1 tablespoon fat-free half-and-half**
- **½ teaspoon salt**
- **½ teaspoon herbes de Provence**
- **1 teaspoon olive oil**
- **½ cup grape tomatoes, halved**
- **¼ cup shredded fat-free cheddar cheese**
- **2 slices high-fiber bread, toasted**
- **Chopped fresh parsley**

1 Beat the eggs, egg whites, half-and-half, salt, and herbes de Provence in a medium bowl until frothy.

2 Heat the oil in a medium nonstick skillet over medium heat. Pour in the egg mixture and cook, stirring gently with a heatproof rubber spatula, until the underside is set, about 2 minutes.

3 Sprinkle the tomatoes and cheddar evenly over half of the omelette. Fold the unfilled half of the omelette over the filling and continue to cook until the eggs are set, about 1 minute longer.

4 Slide the omelette onto a plate and sprinkle with parsley; cut in half. Serve with the toast.

PER SERVING (½ omelette and 1 slice toast): 213 Cal, 9 g Fat, 2 g Sat Fat, 0 g Trans Fat, 215 mg Chol, 1032 mg Sod, 18 g Carb, 4 g Fib, 17 g Prot, 188 mg Calc. *POINTS* value: *4.*

Filling Extra

Serve with a side dish of ½ cup fresh raspberries or strawberries tossed with a little grated orange zest.

Hash Brown and Egg Skillet Breakfast

PREP 15 MIN | **COOK** 25 MIN | **SERVES** 4

- **2 teaspoons sunflower or canola oil**
- **½ onion, chopped**
- **1 garlic clove, minced**
- **3 russet potatoes, scrubbed, shredded, and squeezed dry**
- **½ teaspoon salt**
- **¼ teaspoon black pepper**
- **Pinch ground sage**
- **4 large eggs**
- **4 scallions, sliced**

1 Heat the oil in a large nonstick skillet over medium heat. Add the onion and garlic; cook, stirring, until softened, about 5 minutes.

2 Add the potatoes, salt, pepper, and sage to the skillet; cook, stirring frequently, until the potatoes are softened, about 5 minutes. With a spatula, press down on the potatoes to make an even layer. Continue to cook, without stirring, until the potatoes are lightly browned, about 5 minutes longer.

3 Place a large plate on top of the potato cake and carefully turn the skillet over. Slide the potato cake back into the skillet. With a spoon, make 4 indentations in the potato cake that are large enough to hold an egg.

4 Break 1 egg into each indentation. Sprinkle the eggs and potatoes with the scallions. Cover the skillet and cook until the eggs are set, about 5 minutes.

PER SERVING (¼ of skillet): 223 Cal, 8 g Fat, 2 g Sat Fat, 0 g Trans Fat, 212 mg Chol, 369 mg Sod, 30 g Carb, 4 g Fib, 9 g Prot, 73 mg Calc. *POINTS* value: *4.*

Filling Extra

To bulk up this breakfast, cook 1 red or green bell pepper, diced, along with the onion and garlic. This recipe works with the Simply Filling technique.

Veggie Breakfast Burrito

PREP 10 MIN | **COOK** 5 MIN | **SERVES** 1

- **1 teaspoon canola oil**
- **½ cup fat-free egg substitute**
- **⅛ teaspoon salt**
- **⅛ teaspoon black pepper**
- **1 (7-inch) whole-wheat tortilla, warmed**
- **3 tablespoons shredded fat-free cheddar cheese**
- **½ small tomato, chopped**
- **¼ cup diced green bell pepper**
- **2 scallions, thinly sliced**

1 Heat the oil in a medium nonstick skillet over medium heat.

2 Whisk together the egg substitute, salt, and black pepper in a small bowl until frothy. Pour the egg mixture into the skillet and cook, stirring, until just set, about 2 minutes.

3 Place the warm tortilla on a plate and place the egg on top. Top with the cheddar, tomato, bell pepper, and scallions. Roll the tortilla up to enclose the filling

PER SERVING (1 burrito): 233 Cal, 5 g Fat, 1 g Sat Fat, 0 g Trans Fat, 4 mg Chol, 923 mg Sod, 29 g Carb, 4 g Fib, 23 g Prot, 263 mg Calc. *POINTS* value: *4.*

Filling Extra

Refreshing orange sections are the perfect side for this burrito (1 cup fresh orange sections will increase the *POINTS* value by *1*).

Bacon, Cheddar, and Egg–Topped English Muffins

PREP 5 MIN | **COOK** 10 MIN | **SERVES** 2

- **2 large eggs**
- **1 teaspoon sunflower oil**
- **2 (1-ounce) slices Canadian bacon**
- **1 whole-wheat English muffin, split and toasted**
- **2 (¾-ounce) slices fat-free cheddar cheese**
- **Snipped fresh chives**

1 Fill a medium skillet with 1½ inches of water and bring to a boil. Reduce the heat so the water is barely simmering.

2 Break each egg into a separate small cup. Slip the eggs, one at a time, into the water. Cook until the yolks just begin to set, about 2 minutes. With a slotted spoon, transfer the eggs to paper towels to drain.

3 Wipe out the skillet. Heat the oil in the skillet over medium-high heat. Add the Canadian bacon and cook until heated through, about 1½ minutes on each side.

4 Place a muffin half on each of 2 plates and top each with a slice of cheddar. Top with 1 slice of bacon and 1 egg. Sprinkle with chives.

PER SERVING (1 topped muffin half): 243 Cal, 10 g Fat, 3 g Sat Fat, 0 g Trans Fat, 230 mg Chol, 877 mg Sod, 17 g Carb, 2 g Fib, 20 g Prot, 265 mg Calc. *POINTS* value: *5.*

Filling Extra

Top each muffin half with a slice or two of tomato before adding the cheddar, bacon, and egg.

BACON, CHEDDAR, AND EGG–TOPPED ENGLISH MUFFINS

Southwestern-Style Huevos Rancheros

PREP 10 MIN | **COOK** 5 MIN | **SERVES** 1

- **2 scallions, thinly sliced**
- **1 large egg**
- **3 large egg whites**
- **¼ teaspoon chili powder**
- **¼ cup shredded fat-free cheddar cheese**
- **1 (6-inch) corn tortilla, warmed**
- **3 tablespoons fat-free salsa**

1 Spray a medium nonstick skillet with nonstick spray and set over medium heat. Add the scallions and cook, stirring frequently, just until softened, about 2 minutes.

2 Whisk together the egg, egg whites, and chili powder in a medium bowl. Pour the mixture into the skillet and sprinkle with the cheddar. Cook, stirring, until the eggs are set and the cheese is melted, about 2 minutes.

3 Spoon the eggs on the tortilla and top with the salsa.

PER SERVING (1 filled tortilla): 262 Cal, 6 g Fat, 2 g Sat Fat, 0 g Trans Fat, 218 mg Chol, 835 mg Sod, 23 g Carb, 2 g Fib, 29 g Prot, 376 mg Calc. *POINTS* value: *5.*

Cinnamon French Toast

PREP 5 MIN | **COOK** 20 MIN | **SERVES** 4

- **2 cups fat-free egg substitute**
- **¼ cup fat-free milk**
- **1 teaspoon cinnamon**
- **½ teaspoon vanilla extract**
- **8 slices whole-wheat bread**
- **½ cup reduced-calorie pancake syrup, warmed**

1 Whisk together the egg substitute, milk, cinnamon, and vanilla in a large shallow bowl or pie plate. Dip the bread into the egg mixture, one slice at a time, until evenly soaked.

2 Spray a large nonstick skillet with nonstick spray and set over medium heat. Add the soaked bread to the skillet, in batches, and cook until browned, about 2 minutes on each side.

3 Transfer the French toast to 4 plates and serve with the warm syrup.

PER SERVING (2 slices toast and 2 tablespoons syrup): 263 Cal, 2 g Fat, 0 g Sat Fat, 0 g Trans Fat, 0 mg Chol, 575 mg Sod, 42 g Carb, 5 g Fib, 20 g Prot, 287 mg Calc. *POINTS* value: *5.*

Waffles with Blueberries and Maple Cream

PREP 10 MIN | **COOK** 5 MIN | **SERVES** 4

- **2 cups fat-free ricotta cheese**
- **¼ cup maple syrup**
- **½ teaspoon cinnamon**
- **⅛ teaspoon nutmeg**
- **4 frozen (4-inch) low-fat whole-wheat waffles**
- **1 pint blueberries**
- **¼ cup pecans, chopped**

1 Stir together the ricotta, maple syrup, cinnamon, and nutmeg in a small bowl.

2 Toast the waffles according to the package directions.

3 Place a waffle on each of 4 plates and top evenly with the ricotta mixture. Sprinkle evenly with the blueberries and pecans.

PER SERVING (1 waffle, ½ cup blueberries, and 1 tablespoon pecans): 322 Cal, 6 g Fat, 1 g Sat Fat, 0 g Trans Fat, 12 mg Chol, 322 mg Sod, 48 g Carb, 4 g Fib, 20 g Prot, 278 mg Calc. *POINTS* value: *6.*

In the Kitchen

If you can't find fresh blueberries in your market, substitute another fresh berry or use thawed frozen unsweetened blueberries, found in the freezer case.

Wild Blueberry and Cornmeal Pancakes

PREP 25 MIN | **COOK** 20 MIN | **SERVES** 4

- **1 cup reduced-fat all-purpose baking mix**
- **1 cup yellow cornmeal, preferably stone ground**
- **1¼ cups low-fat (1%) milk**
- **1 large egg, beaten**
- **3 tablespoons sugar**
- **1¼ cups fresh or frozen wild blueberries**

1 Stir together the baking mix, cornmeal, milk, egg, and sugar in a large bowl just until moistened. Gently stir in the blueberries.

2 Spray a nonstick griddle or large nonstick skillet with nonstick spray and set over medium heat. Drop the batter by heaping ¼ cupfuls onto the griddle and cook the pancakes until bubbles appear and the edges look dry, about 3 minutes. Turn and cook until browned, about 2 minutes longer. Repeat with the remaining batter to make 12 pancakes in all.

PER SERVING (3 pancakes): 341 Cal, 5 g Fat, 2 g Sat Fat, 0 g Trans Fat, 56 mg Chol, 388 mg Sod, 64 g Carb, 4 g Fib, 10 g Prot, 136 mg Calc. *POINTS* value: *6.*

In the Kitchen

Wild blueberries are often available in the freezer section of large supermarkets. They are appreciated for their intense sweet-tart flavor. If you happen to have regular blueberries on hand, they can also be used here.

Brown Rice 'n' Honey Pancakes

PREP 25 MIN | **COOK** 20 MIN | **SERVES** 2

- **½ cup cooked brown rice**
- **1 cup fat-free milk**
- **2 tablespoons honey**
- **⅓ cup all-purpose flour**
- **3 tablespoons wheat germ**
- **1 teaspoon baking powder**
- **¼ teaspoon salt**
- **¼ cup fat-free egg substitute**
- **1 cup unsweetened applesauce**
- **2 tablespoons ground flaxseed**

1 Combine the rice, milk, and honey in a small saucepan and bring to a boil over medium-high heat. Reduce the heat and simmer 5 minutes. Transfer the mixture to a bowl and let cool about 10 minutes.

2 Meanwhile, whisk together the flour, wheat germ, baking powder, and salt in a medium bowl. Stir in the lukewarm rice mixture and egg substitute.

3 Spray a nonstick griddle or large nonstick skillet with nonstick spray and set over medium heat. Drop the batter by ¼ cupfuls onto the griddle and cook the pancakes until bubbles appear and the edges look dry, about 3 minutes. Turn and cook until deep golden brown, about 2 minutes longer.

4 Transfer the pancakes to 2 plates and top evenly with the applesauce and flaxseed.

PER SERVING (3 pancakes and ½ cup applesauce): 379 Cal, 5 g Fat, 1 g Sat Fat, 0 g Trans Fat, 2 mg Chol, 792 mg Sod, 73 g Carb, 7 g Fib, 15 g Prot, 373 mg Calc. *POINTS* value: 7.

Filling Extra

Top each serving of applesauce with ½ cup sliced strawberries.

BROWN RICE 'N' HONEY PANCAKES

Peach Muesli with Almonds

PREP 35 MIN | **COOK** NONE | **SERVES** 6

- **2** **cups rolled (old-fashioned) oats**
- **¾** **cup chopped dried peaches**
- **¼** **cup golden raisins**
- **1** **cup fat-free milk**
- **¼** **cup apple juice**
- **1** **cup plain fat-free yogurt**
- **2** **tablespoons honey**
- **¼** **cup sliced almonds**

1 Stir together the oats, peaches, raisins, milk, and apple juice in a medium bowl; let stand 30 minutes, stirring occasionally.

2 Meanwhile, stir together the yogurt and honey in a small bowl.

3 Divide the oat mixture evenly among 6 cereal bowls. Top evenly with the yogurt mixture and almonds.

PER SERVING (½ cup): 255 Cal, 4 g Fat, 1 g Sat Fat, 0 g Trans Fat, 2 mg Chol, 53 mg Sod, 48 g Carb, 5 g Fib, 10 g Prot, 165 mg Calc. *POINTS* value: *5.*

Filling Extra

Top the muesli with sliced banana (½ large banana for each serving will increase the *POINTS* value by *1*).

Morning Chai

PREP 5 MIN | **COOK** 15 MIN | **SERVES** 4

- **4** **cups cold water**
- **5** **regular or decaffeinated black tea bags**
- **1** **(3-inch) cinnamon stick, broken in half**
- **8** **whole cardamom pods, crushed**
- **12** **whole black peppercorns**
- **1½** **cups vanilla soy milk**

Combine all the ingredients except the milk in a large saucepan and bring to a boil over high heat. Boil 10 minutes; stir in the soy milk. Cook, stirring, until heated through, about 1 minute longer. Pour through a sieve into 4 cups or mugs.

PER SERVING (1 cup): 63 Cal, 2 g Fat, 0 g Sat Fat, 0 g Trans Fat, 0 mg Chol, 60 mg Sod, 10 g Carb, 1 g Fib, 3 g Prot, 118 mg Calc. *POINTS* value: *1.*

In the Kitchen

Now served in trendy coffee bars, chai is a traditional drink from southern India. It's a great way to get antioxidants while enjoying your milk spicy and satisfying. Chai is also delicious served over ice in a tall glass.

CREAMY COUSCOUS
BREAKFAST PUDDING

Creamy Couscous Breakfast Pudding

PREP 15 MIN | **COOK** 20 MIN | **SERVES** 6

- **1½ cups water**
- **1 cup whole-wheat couscous**
- **Pinch salt**
- **3 cups fat-free milk**
- **2 tablespoons packed brown sugar**
- **½ teaspoon grated orange zest**
- **¼ cup fat-free egg substitute**
- **¼ cup toasted wheat germ**
- **¾ teaspoon vanilla extract**
- **¼ cup sliced almonds (optional)**

1 Bring the water to a boil in a large heavy saucepan over high heat. Stir in the couscous and salt. Reduce the heat and simmer until the water is absorbed, about 2 minutes. Remove the saucepan from the heat and fluff the couscous with a fork. Cover and let stand about 5 minutes.

2 Whisk the milk, brown sugar, and orange zest into the couscous. Bring to a boil over medium-high heat, whisking frequently to break up any lumps. Reduce the heat to medium-low and cook, stirring frequently, until the mixture is slightly thickened, about 5 minutes. Remove the saucepan from the heat.

3 Whisk together ½ cup of the couscous mixture and the egg substitute in a small bowl. Return the mixture to the saucepan and cook over low heat, stirring, until the pudding is thick and creamy, about 5 minutes longer.

4 Stir in the wheat germ and vanilla. Serve topped with the almonds, if using.

PER SERVING (generous ¾ cup pudding without almonds): 152 Cal, 1 g Fat, 0 g Sat Fat, 0 g Trans Fat, 2 mg Chol, 123 mg Sod, 28 g Carb, 3 g Fib, 9 g Prot, 190 mg Calc.
POINTS value: *3.*

Filling Extra

Top each serving of pudding with ½ cup fresh raspberries or strawberries.

Peanut Butter Blast

PREP 5 MIN | **COOK** NONE | **SERVES** 1

1 small banana
½ cup vanilla fat-free yogurt
½ cup fat-free milk
1 tablespoon creamy peanut butter
¼ teaspoon vanilla extract
Pinch cinnamon

Combine all the ingredients except the cinnamon in a blender and process until very smooth. Pour into a glass and sprinkle with the cinnamon.

PER SERVING (about 1 cup): 328 Cal, 9 g Fat, 2 g Sat Fat, 0 g Trans Fat, 5 mg Chol, 190 mg Sod, 53 g Carb, 6 g Fib, 14 g Prot, 356 mg Calc. *POINTS* value: *7.*

In the Kitchen

Here's an easy way to keep ripe bananas. Place unpeeled bananas in the freezer for up to 1 month. You can use a frozen banana to make this refreshing chilled drink.

Soy-Blueberry Breakfast Shake

PREP 5 MIN | **COOK** NONE | **SERVES** 1

- **1 cup calcium-fortified plain fat-free soy milk**
- **1 cup frozen unsweetened blueberries**
- **½ banana**
- **2 teaspoons honey**
- **1 teaspoon vanilla extract**

Combine all the ingredients in a blender and process until smooth. Pour into a tall glass.

PER SERVING (about 2 cups): 296 Cal, 1 g Fat, 0 g Sat Fat, 0 g Trans Fat, 0 mg Chol, 62 mg Sod, 67 g Carb, 7 g Fib, 7 g Prot, 413 mg Calc. *POINTS* value: *5.*

In the Kitchen

For a change of pace, substitute other fresh berries—or a combination—for the blueberries. Try strawberries, raspberries, or blackberries.

chapter 2

brown bag it !

Taking a sandwich or soup to work never tasted so good!

Best BLTs

PREP 5 MIN | **COOK** NONE | **SERVES** 2

- **4 teaspoons fat-free mayonnaise**
- **2 teaspoons pesto**
- **4 slices whole-wheat bread**
- **½ cup lightly packed baby arugula**
- **¼ avocado, halved, pitted, peeled, and thinly sliced**
- **1 tomato, sliced**
- **6 slices turkey bacon, crisp cooked**

1 Stir together the mayonnaise and pesto in a small bowl.

2 Spread the mayonnaise mixture evenly on 2 slices of the bread. Layer the bread evenly with the arugula, avocado, tomato, and bacon. Cover the sandwiches with the remaining slices of bread. Cut each sandwich in half.

PER SERVING (1 sandwich): 280 Cal, 10 g Fat, 2 g Sat Fat, 0 g Trans Fat, 33 mg Chol, 799 mg Sod, 31 g Carb, 5 g Fib, 16 g Prot, 105 mg Calc. *POINTS* value: *6.*

In the Kitchen

Cook the turkey bacon up to several hours ahead and drain on paper towels. When ready to use, microwave on High just until heated through, about 30 seconds.

BEST BLTS

Ham and Swiss Paninis

PREP 5 MIN | **COOK** 10 MIN | **SERVES** 2

- **2 teaspoons unsalted butter, softened**
- **4 slices high-fiber bread**
- **2 slices reduced-fat Swiss cheese**
- **6 (1-ounce) slices lean reduced-sodium ham**

1 Preheat a panini or sandwich press or set a nonstick ridged grill pan over medium heat. Spread ½ teaspoon butter on one side of each slice of bread.

2 Place 2 slices of the bread, buttered side down, on a work surface and layer each with 1 slice Swiss and 3 slices ham. Cover each sandwich with the remaining slices of bread, buttered side out.

3 Place the sandwiches on the press and close the lid or place them on the grill pan and cover with a heavy skillet. Cook until the sandwiches are browned and the cheese is melted, about 5 minutes. (Turn the sandwiches halfway through the cooking time if using a grill pan.) Cut in half and serve.

PER SERVING (1 sandwich): 304 Cal, 11 g Fat, 5 g Sat Fat, 0 g Trans Fat, 58 mg Chol, 806 mg Sod, 31 g Carb, 10 g Fib, 25 g Prot, 404 mg Calc. *POINTS* value: *6.*

Filling Extra

Serve each sandwich with a handful of celery sticks and carrot sticks.

Chicken and Roasted Pepper Sandwiches

PREP 20 MIN | **COOK** NONE | **SERVES** 4

- **¼ cup light cream cheese (Neufchâtel), softened**
- **2 teaspoons grated lemon zest**
- **½ teaspoon Italian seasoning or dried oregano**
- **¼ teaspoon black pepper**
- **8 thin slices whole-wheat bread**
- **1½ cups shredded deli roast chicken breast**
- **½ cup roasted red pepper, thinly sliced**
- **8 large fresh basil leaves**

1 Mash together the cream cheese, lemon zest, Italian seasoning, and black pepper in a small bowl.

2 Spread the cheese mixture evenly over 4 slices of the bread. Layer evenly with the chicken, roasted red pepper, and basil. Cover with the remaining slices of bread. Cut each sandwich in half.

PER SERVING (1 sandwich): 246 Cal, 7 g Fat, 3 g Sat Fat, 0 g Trans Fat, 54 mg Chol, 317 mg Sod, 21 g Carb, 4 g Fib, 23 g Prot, 75 mg Calc. *POINTS* value: *5.*

Filling Extra

Layer each sandwich with baby spinach leaves or other favorite leafy green.

CHICKEN AND
TZATZIKI–STUFFED
PITAS

Chicken and Tzatziki–Stuffed Pitas

PREP 20 MIN | **COOK** NONE | **SERVES** 2

- **¾ cup plain fat-free yogurt**
- **⅓ cup shredded cucumber, gently squeezed dry**
- **1 small garlic clove, minced**
- **¼ teaspoon salt**
- **⅛ teaspoon black pepper**
- **2 (7-inch) whole-wheat pitas, halved**
- **1½ cups shredded cooked chicken breast**
- **1 large tomato, cut into 8 slices**
- **4 small romaine lettuce leaves**
- **¼ cup crumbled fat-free feta cheese**

Stir together the yogurt, cucumber, garlic, salt, and pepper in a small bowl. Cut each pita in half. Spread half of the yogurt mixture inside the pitas. Layer the chicken, tomato, lettuce, and feta evenly inside the pitas. To serve, top with the remaining yogurt mixture

PER SERVING (1 sandwich): 464 Cal, 6 g Fat, 2 g Sat Fat, 0 g Trans Fat, 88 mg Chol, 1070 mg Sod, 54 g Carb, 8 g Fib, 48 g Prot, 280 mg Calc. *POINTS* value: *9.*

In the Kitchen

Fat-free feta cheese is found in the gourmet cheese section of supermarkets.

Asian-Style Duck Roll-Ups

PREP 20 MIN | **COOK** NONE | **SERVES** 4

- **2 cups shredded cooked duck breast or chicken breast**
- **¼ cup hoisin sauce**
- **2 scallions, thinly sliced**
- **4 (7-inch) whole-wheat tortillas, warmed**
- **½ small red bell pepper, thinly sliced**
- **8 arugula leaves, trimmed**

1 Stir together the duck, hoisin, and scallions in a medium bowl.

2 Lay the tortillas on a work surface and spread evenly with the duck mixture. Top evenly with the bell pepper and arugula. Roll up the tortillas and cut in half.

PER SERVING (1 roll-up): 203 Cal, 2 g Fat, 1 g Sat Fat, 0 g Trans Fat, 59 mg Chol, 554 mg Sod, 22 g Carb, 3 g Fib, 24 g Prot, 34 mg Calc. *POINTS* value: *4.*

In the Kitchen

Packaged cooked duck breast is found in specialty food stores. If it comes with the skin on, be sure to remove it before shredding the duck.

Avocado, Spinach, and Feta Wraps

PREP 10 MIN | **COOK** NONE | **SERVES** 2

- **½ avocado, halved, pitted, and peeled**
- **¼ teaspoon salt**
- **¼ teaspoon black pepper**
- **1 (10-inch) spinach tortilla or wrap**
- **1 cup lightly packed baby spinach**
- **1 small zucchini, shredded**
- **¼ cup crumbled fat-free feta cheese**
- **1 tablespoon balsamic vinegar**
- **1 teaspoon olive oil**

Mash together the avocado, salt, and pepper in a small bowl. Spread the mixture evenly on the tortilla. Top with the spinach, zucchini, and feta; drizzle with the vinegar and oil. Roll up the tortilla to enclose the filling. Cut the wrap in half.

PER SERVING (½ wrap): 250 Cal, 15 g Fat, 4 g Sat Fat, 0 g Trans Fat, 13 mg Chol, 577 mg Sod, 26 g Carb, 6 g Fib, 7 g Prot, 166 mg Calc. *POINTS* value: *5.*

Salmon Salad Sandwiches

PREP 15 MIN | **COOK** NONE | **SERVES** 2

- **1 (7½-ounce) can salmon, drained and flaked**
- **3 tablespoons plain fat-free yogurt**
- **½ cup peeled, seeded, and chopped cucumber**
- **2 scallions, thinly sliced**
- **2 tablespoons chopped fresh dill**
- **1 tablespoon capers, drained**
- **Zest and juice of ½ lemon**
- **½ (10-ounce) whole-wheat baguette**

1 Stir together all the ingredients except the whole-wheat baguette in a medium bowl.

2 Split the baguette lengthwise in half and remove the soft bready center. Spoon the salmon mixture into the bottom half of the baguette and cover with the top of the baguette. Cut the sandwich in half.

PER SERVING (½ sandwich): 321 Cal, 7 g Fat, 1 g Sat Fat, 0 g Trans Fat, 73 mg Chol, 839 mg Sod, 34 g Carb, 6 g Fib, 32 g Prot, 389 mg Calc. *POINTS* value: *6.*

Filling Extra

Serve each sandwich with some cherry tomatoes.

Thai-Style Shrimp Salad Pitas

PREP 20 MIN | **COOK** NONE | **SERVES** 4

- **¼ cup reduced-fat mayonnaise**
- **¼ cup lime juice**
- **¼ cup chopped fresh cilantro**
- **1 tablespoon Thai fish sauce**
- **¼ teaspoon black pepper**
- **1 pound frozen cooked medium shrimp, thawed and chopped**
- **½ small green bell pepper, chopped**
- **½ small red onion, chopped**
- **4 (7-inch) whole-wheat pitas**
- **4 green leaf lettuce leaves**

1 Stir together the mayonnaise, lime juice, cilantro, fish sauce, and black pepper in a large bowl. Add the shrimp, bell pepper, and onion to the mayonnaise mixture and toss to coat.

2 Cut off the top third of each pita and discard. Line each pita with a lettuce leaf and fill evenly with the shrimp salad.

PER SERVING (1 pita): 342 Cal, 8 g Fat, 1 g Sat Fat, 0 g Trans Fat, 226 mg Chol, 1067 mg Sod, 40 g Carb, 6 g Fib, 31 g Prot, 71 mg Calc. *POINTS* value: *7.*

CALIFORNIA
HEALTH
SANDWICHES

California Health Sandwiches

PREP 20 MIN | **COOK** NONE | **SERVES** 2

- **1** **cup alfalfa sprouts**
- **½** **cup shredded carrot**
- **2** **tablespoons fat-free Italian dressing**
- **2** **tablespoons hummus**
- **4** **slices whole-grain bread, toasted**
- **½** **small avocado, thinly sliced**
- **1** **tomato, thinly sliced**
- **½** **teaspoon salt**
- **⅛** **teaspoon black pepper**

1 Put the alfalfa sprouts and carrot in separate small bowls; toss with the dressing.

2 Spread the hummus evenly on the slices of bread. Layer evenly with the avocado, tomato, carrot and alfalfa mixture. Sprinkle with the salt and pepper.

PER SERVING: (1 sandwich). 258 Cal, 9 g Fat, 1 g Sat Fat, 0 g Trans Fat, 0 mg Chol, 1100 mg Sod, 35 g Carb, 9 g Fib, 10 g Prot, 101 mg Calc. *POINTS* value: *5.*

Hearty Corn Chowder

PREP 20 MIN | **COOK** 20 MIN | **SERVES** 4

- **2 teaspoons olive oil**
- **1 red or green bell pepper, diced**
- **1 onion, chopped**
- **3 cups frozen corn kernels**
- **¾ pound red potatoes, scrubbed and diced**
- **1 cup reduced-sodium chicken broth**
- **½ teaspoon salt**
- **¼ teaspoon black pepper**
- **3 cups fat-free milk**
- **4 slices turkey bacon, crisp cooked and coarsely crumbled**

1 Heat the oil in a large nonstick saucepan over medium heat. Add the bell pepper and onion; cook, stirring, until softened, about 5 minutes. Add the corn, potatoes, broth, salt, and black pepper; bring to a boil over medium-high heat. Reduce the heat and simmer, covered, until the potatoes are tender, about 10 minutes.

2 Puree ½ cup of the vegetable mixture with 1 cup of the milk in a blender until almost smooth. Stir the puree along with the remaining 2 cups milk back into the soup. Cook over medium heat, stirring occasionally, until heated through, about 5 minutes. Serve sprinkled with the bacon.

PER SERVING (about 2 cups): 319 Cal, 7 g Fat, 2 g Sat Fat, 0 g Trans Fat, 17 mg Chol, 839 mg Sod, 52 g Carb, 6 g Fib, 16 g Prot, 266 mg Calc. *POINTS* value: *6.*

In the Kitchen

Fresh corn kernels can also be used in this soup. You will need about 6 medium ears to get 3 cups of kernels.

Beef-Vegetable Soup

PREP 25 MIN | **COOK** 35 MIN | **SERVES** 6

- **1 tablespoon olive oil**
- **¾ pound top round steak, trimmed and cut into ½-inch pieces**
- **4 carrots, thinly sliced**
- **4 celery stalks, sliced**
- **3 parsnips, diced**
- **1 large onion, chopped**
- **½ teaspoon dried thyme**
- **5 cups reduced-sodium beef broth**
- **1 (14½-ounce) can petite diced tomatoes**
- **½ teaspoon salt**
- **¼ teaspoon black pepper**
- **2 cups lightly packed baby spinach**
- **1½ cups hot cooked brown rice**

1 Heat the oil in a large nonstick saucepan over medium heat. Add the beef, in batches, and cook, stirring, until browned, about 4 minutes. With a slotted spoon, transfer the beef to a plate.

2 Add the carrots, celery, parsnips, onion, and thyme to the Dutch oven; cook, stirring, until slightly softened, about 5 minutes. Add the beef and any accumulated juices, the broth, tomatoes, salt, and pepper; bring to a boil. Reduce the heat and simmer 10 minutes. Stir in the spinach and cook until the beef is tender, about 10 minutes longer. Stir in the rice.

PER SERVING (about 1⅓ cups): 255 Cal, 6 g Fat, 1 g Sat Fat, 0 g Trans Fat, 31 mg Chol, 658 mg Sod, 38 g Carb, 7 g Fib, 20 g Prot, 95 mg Calc. *POINTS* value: *5.*

Tip

This recipe works with the Simply Filling technique.

Manhattan Clam Chowder

PREP 20 MIN | **COOK** 30 MIN | **SERVES** 4

- **2 teaspoons olive oil**
- **1 onion, finely chopped**
- **1 carrot, finely chopped**
- **1 celery stalk, finely chopped**
- **1 large all-purpose potato, peeled and finely chopped**
- **1 (14½-ounce) can petite diced tomatoes**
- **1 (8-ounce) bottle clam juice**
- **1½ cups water**
- **½ teaspoon dried thyme**
- **¼ teaspoon black pepper**
- **2 (6½-ounce) cans chopped clams, undrained**

1 Heat the oil in a large nonstick saucepan over medium heat. Add the onion, carrot, and celery; cook, stirring, until softened, about 5 minutes. Add the potato and cook, stirring, 2 minutes longer.

2 Add all the remaining ingredients except the clams; bring to a boil over medium-high heat. Reduce the heat and simmer, partially covered, until the vegetables are tender, about 15 minutes.

3 Add the clams and simmer just until heated through, about 2 minutes (do not boil or the clams will toughen).

PER SERVING (about 1¾ cups): 174 Cal, 3 g Fat, 0 g Sat Fat, 0 g Trans Fat, 25 mg Chol, 358 mg Sod, 25 g Carb, 4 g Fib, 12 g Prot, 99 mg Calc. *POINTS* value: *3.*

Tip

This recipe works with the Simply Filling technique.

Chickpea Soup

PREP 15 MIN | **COOK** 10 MIN | **SERVES** 4

- **5 cups reduced-sodium chicken broth**
- **2 (15½-ounce) cans chickpeas, rinsed and drained**
- **2 teaspoons olive oil**
- **2 carrots, thinly sliced**
- **1 rcd bcll pcppcr, ohoppod**
- **1 onion, chopped**
- **3 garlic cloves, minced**
- **2 teaspoons fresh rosemary**
- **½ teaspoon salt**
- **¼ teaspoon black pepper**
- **2 tablespoons chopped fresh parsley**

1 Puree the broth with the chickpeas, in batches, in a blender.

2 Heat the oil in a large nonstick saucepan over medium heat. Add the carrots, bell pepper, onion, and garlic; cook, stirring, until the carrots are crisp-tender, about 5 minutes.

3 Stir in the chickpea mixture, rosemary, salt, and black pepper. Stir in a little water if the soup is too thick. Cook over medium heat until heated through, about 4 minutes. Serve sprinkled with the parsley.

PER SERVING (about 1½ cups): 315 Cal, 6 g Fat, 1 g Sat Fat, 0 g Trans Fat, 0 mg Chol, 1023 mg Sod, 49 g Carb, 11 g Fib, 18 g Prot, 124 mg Calc. *POINTS* value: *6.*

Filling Extra

Add 1 cup drained petite diced tomatoes along with the chickpea mixture. This recipe works with the Simply Filling technique.

CREAMY TOMATO SOUP
AND HAM AND SWISS
PANINIS, PAGE 40

Creamy Tomato Soup

PREP 15 MIN | **COOK** 15 MIN | **SERVES** 4

- **2 teaspoons olive oil**
- **1 onion, chopped**
- **2 garlic cloves, minced**
- **4 large tomatoes, coarsely chopped**
- **1 cup reduced-sodium chicken broth**
- **4 teaspoons chopped fresh thyme or 1 teaspoon dried**
- **1 teaspoon salt**
- **¼ teaspoon black pepper**
- **3 cups fat-free milk**
- **¼ cup tomato paste**

1 Heat the oil in a large nonstick saucepan over medium heat. Add the onion and garlic; cook, stirring, until softened, about 5 minutes.

2 Stir in the tomatoes, broth, thyme, salt, and pepper. Cover and simmer until the vegetables are tender, about 5 minutes longer. Let cool 5 minutes.

3 Puree the tomato mixture, in batches, in a blender. Return the mixture to the saucepan.

4 Whisk together the milk and tomato paste in a small bowl; whisk it into the soup. Cook, stirring occasionally, just until heated through, about 5 minutes (do not boil).

PER SERVING (1¼ cups): 198 Cal, 6 g Fat, 1 g Sat Fat, 0 g Trans Fat, 4 mg Chol, 861 mg Sod, 29 g Carb, 4 g Fib, 11 g Prot, 263 mg Calc. *POINTS* value: *4.*

Filling Extra

If you love the idea of tomato-rice soup, stir 2 cups hot cooked brown rice into the soup in step 4. The per-serving *POINTS* value will increase by *1.* This recipe works with the Simply Filling technique.

Potato-Watercress Soup

PREP 10 MIN | **COOK** 30 MIN | **SERVES** 4

- **2 teaspoons olive oil**
- **1 onion, chopped**
- **4 Yukon Gold potatoes, peeled and coarsely chopped**
- **1 bunch watercress, tender sprigs only**
- **4 cups reduced-sodium chicken broth**
- **1 cup fat-free half-and-half**
- **½ teaspoon salt**
- **⅛ teaspoon black pepper**

1 Heat the oil in a large nonstick saucepan over medium heat. Add the onion and cook, stirring, until softened, about 5 minutes. Add the potatoes, watercress, and broth; bring to a boil over medium-high heat. Reduce the heat and simmer, covered, until the potatoes are tender, about 15 minutes; let cool 5 minutes.

2 Puree the potato mixture, in batches, in a blender. Return the soup to the saucepan and stir in the half-and-half, salt, and pepper. Cook over medium heat until heated through, about 4 minutes.

PER SERVING (about 1¼ cups): 230 Cal, 3 g Fat, 1 g Sat Fat, 0 g Trans Fat, 3 mg Chol, 954 mg Sod, 43 g Carb, 4 g Fib, 8 g Prot, 123 mg Calc. *POINTS* value: *4.*

In the Kitchen

Enjoy this soup well chilled and it becomes a tasty variation on the classic French potato-leek soup known as vichyssoise.

Cremini Mushroom, Tomato, and Rice Soup

PREP 10 MIN | **COOK** 25 MIN | **SERVES** 4

- **2 teaspoons olive oil**
- **2 leeks (white and pale green parts only) halved lengthwise, chopped, and well rinsed**
- **1 pound cremini mushrooms, sliced**
- **1 (14½-ounce) can fire-roasted diced tomatoes**
- **2½ cups reduced-sodium chicken broth**
- **¼ teaspoon salt**
- **⅛ teaspoon black pepper**
- **½ cup quick-cooking brown rice**

1 Heat the oil in a large nonstick saucepan over medium-high heat. Add the leeks and cook, stirring, until softened, about 5 minutes. Add the mushrooms and cook, stirring, until tender, about 5 minutes.

2 Add the tomatoes, broth, salt, and pepper; simmer 5 minutes. Stir in the rice and cook until tender, about 10 minutes longer.

PER SERVING (1½ cups): 145 Cal, 3 g Fat, 0 g Sat Fat, 0 g Trans Fat, 0 mg Chol, 657 mg Sod, 24 g Carb, 4 g Fib, 8 g Prot, 78 mg Calc. *POINTS* value: *2.*

In the Kitchen

Leeks, a flavorful member of the onion family, resemble very large scallions. Be sure to rinse the leeks thoroughly, as they tend to be sandy. This recipe works with the Simply Filling technique.

chapter 3

hearty salads and microwave meals

Easy does it dishes for the whole family

TROPICAL
TURKEY SALAD

Tropical Turkey Salad

PREP 20 MIN | **COOK** NONE | **SERVES** 4

- **3 tablespoons lemon juice**
- **2 teaspoons olive oil**
- **½ teaspoon salt**
- **¼ teaspoon black pepper**
- **2 cups diced cooked turkey breast**
- **1 large Granny Smith apple, cored and sliced**
- **1 mango, peeled, pitted, and diced**
- **1 papaya, peeled, halved, seeded, and cut into chunks**
- **½ cup chopped red onion**
- **1 jalapeño pepper, seeded and minced**
- **Red leaf lettuce leaves**

1 To make the dressing, whisk together the lemon juice, oil, salt, and black pepper in a serving bowl.

2 Add the remaining ingredients to the dressing and toss to coat. Line 4 bowls with red leaf lettuce. Top evenly with the turkey salad.

PER SERVING (1½ cups): 283 Cal, 6 g Fat, 1 g Sat Fat, 0 g Trans Fat, 60 mg Chol, 482 mg Sod, 30 g Carb, 11 g Fib, 27 g Prot, 58 mg Calc. *POINTS* value: *5.*

Filling Extra

To boost the serving size, toss a 15½-ounce can of red kidney beans or black beans, rinsed and drained into the salad. The per-serving *POINTS* value will increase by ***1.*** This recipe works with the Simply Filling technique.

Pasta Salad with Apple and Chicken

PREP 10 MIN | **COOK** NONE | **SERVES** 4

- **⅓ cup orange juice**
- **3 tablespoons balsamic vinegar**
- **1 tablespoon Dijon mustard**
- **1 tablespoon maple syrup**
- **3 cups leftover cooked whole-wheat penne**
- **1 cup diced cooked chicken breast**
- **¼ cup pecans, coarsely chopped**
- **1 small Granny Smith apple, cored and chopped**
- **1 large shallot, finely chopped**
- **1 (5-ounce) bag baby arugula**

1 To make the dressing, whisk together the orange juice, vinegar, mustard, and maple syrup in a large bowl.

2 Add the pasta, chicken, pecans, apple, and shallot to the dressing; toss to coat.

3 Divide the arugula evenly among 4 plates. Spoon the pasta salad evenly on top.

PER SERVING (1 cup arugula and 1¼ cups pasta salad): 315 Cal, 8 g Fat, 1 g Sat Fat, 0 g Trans Fat, 29 mg Chol, 284 mg Sod, 46 g Carb, 5 g Fib, 19 g Prot, 100 mg Calc. *POINTS* value: *6.*

In the Kitchen

If you don't happen to have cooked pasta at hand, substitute 2½ cups prepared whole-wheat couscous for the same *POINTS* value.

PASTA SALAD
WITH APPLE
AND CHICKEN

Smoked Turkey, Carrot, and Raisin Salad

PREP 20 MIN | **COOK** NONE | **SERVES** 4

- **⅓ cup reduced-fat mayonnaise**
- **1 teaspoon grated lemon zest**
- **1 tablespoon lemon juice**
- **½ teaspoon salt**
- **⅛ teaspoon black pepper**
- **1 (6-ounce) piece smoked turkey breast, diced**
- **6 carrots, shredded (about 3 cups)**
- **⅓ cup dark raisins**
- **8 cups lightly packed baby romaine**
- **¼ cup coarsely chopped unsalted peanuts**

1 To make the dressing, whisk together the mayonnaise, lemon zest and juice, salt, and pepper in a large bowl.

2 Add the turkey, carrots, and raisins to the dressing; toss to coat.

3 Divide the salad greens evenly among 4 plates. Top with the turkey mixture and sprinkle evenly with the peanuts.

PER SERVING (about 3 cups): 199 Cal, 9 g Fat, 2 g Sat Fat, 0 g Trans Fat, 28 mg Chol, 696 mg Sod, 22 g Carb, 4 g Fib, 10 g Prot, 75 mg Calc. *POINTS* value: *4.*

Filling Extra

Add 1 red apple, diced, to the turkey mixture for extra crunch and fresh flavor.

Gingery Turkey-Couscous Salad

PREP 10 MIN | **COOK** NONE | **SERVES** 2

- **½ cup whole-wheat couscous**
- **5 teaspoons unseasoned rice vinegar**
- **5 teaspoons reduced-sodium soy sauce**
- **1 garlic clove, minced**
- **2 teaspoons minced peeled fresh ginger**
- **1½ cups shredded cooked turkey breast**
- **1½ cups small broccoli florets**
- **1 large red bell pepper, cut into ½-inch pieces**
- **3 scallions, thinly sliced**
- **¼ cup chopped fresh cilantro**

1 Prepare the couscous according to the package directions, omitting the fat and salt if desired. Let the couscous cool completely.

2 Meanwhile, to make the dressing, whisk together the vinegar, soy sauce, garlic, and ginger in a serving bowl. Add the cooled couscous and the remaining ingredients; toss to coat.

PER SERVING (2 cups): 357 Cal, 8 g Fat, 2 g Sat Fat, 0 g Trans Fat, 86 mg Chol, 279 mg Sod, 34 g Carb, 8 g Fib, 39 g Prot, 93 mg Calc. *POINTS* value: 7.

Tip

This recipe works with the Simply Filling technique.

LIGHT AND
LUSCIOUS
COBB SALAD

Light and Luscious Cobb Salad

PREP 25 MIN | **COOK** NONE | **SERVES** 4

- **3 tablespoons sherry vinegar**
- **2 teaspoons olive oil**
- **½ teaspoon salt**
- **¼ teaspoon black pepper**
- **6 cups torn romaine lettuce**
- **2 cups diced cooked turkey breast**
- **2 large tomatoes, diced**
- **½ avocado, halved, pitted, peeled, and diced**
- **2 large hard-cooked egg whites, chopped**
- **6 slices turkey bacon, crisp cooked and coarsely crumbled**
- **¼ cup crumbled blue cheese**

1 To make the dressing, whisk together the vinegar, oil, salt, and pepper in a small bowl.

2 Spread the lettuce on a platter. Arrange the turkey, tomatoes, and avocado in rows on top of the lettuce. Sprinkle with the egg whites, bacon, and blue cheese. Serve the dressing on the side.

PER SERVING (about 1½ cups): 292 Cal, 14 g Fat, 4 g Sat Fat, 0 g Trans Fat, 85 mg Chol, 1083 mg Sod, 8 g Carb, 4 g Fib, 32 g Prot, 94 mg Calc.
POINTS value: *6.*

Salmon with Corn, Black Bean, and Tomato Salad

PREP 20 MIN | **COOK** NONE | **SERVES** 6

- **2 tablespoons lime juice**
- **1 teaspoon olive oil**
- **1 teaspoon salt**
- **¼ teaspoon black pepper**
- **1 (15½-ounce) can black beans, rinsed and drained**
- **2 cups drained canned corn kernels**
- **1 large tomato, diced**
- **½ small red onion, finely chopped**
- **½ cup coarsely chopped fresh cilantro**
- **1 jalapeño pepper, seeded and minced**
- **6 large Boston lettuce leaves**
- **6 (3-ounce) prepared poached salmon fillets**

1 To make the dressing, whisk together the lime juice, oil, salt, and black pepper in a large bowl.

2 Add the beans, corn, tomato, onion, cilantro, and jalapeño pepper to the dressing; toss to coat.

3 Divide the lettuce among 6 plates; top with the salmon. Spoon the bean salad next to the fish.

PER SERVING (1 salmon fillet and about 1¼ cups salad): 311 Cal, 9 g Fat, 2 g Sat Fat, 0 g Trans Fat, 83 mg Chol, 635 mg Sod, 26 g Carb, 7 g Fib, 33 g Prot, 61 mg Calc. *POINTS* value: *6.*

Tip

This recipe works with the Simply Filling technique.

Tuna-Potato Salad

PREP 20 MIN | **COOK** NONE | **SERVES** 4

- **¼ cup fat-free mayonnaise**
- **¼ teaspoon salt**
- **¼ teaspoon black pepper**
- **2 (6-ounce) cans water-packed solid white tuna, drained and flaked**
- **1 pound packaged cooked diced potatoes**
- **2 large shallots, finely chopped**
- **4 cups mixed baby salad greens**
- **Lemon wedges**

1 To make the dressing, whisk together the mayonnaise, salt, and pepper in a large bowl.

2 Add the tuna, potatoes, and shallots to the dressing and stir to combine well.

3 Divide the salad greens evenly among 4 plates. Top evenly with the tuna-potato mixture. Serve with lemon wedges.

PER SERVING (1¼ cups): 195 Cal, 1 g Fat, 0 g Sat Fat, 0 g Trans Fat, 22 mg Chol, 526 mg Sod, 26 g Carb, 4 g Fib, 20 g Prot, 64 mg Calc. *POINTS* value: *3.*

Filling Extra

Surround each serving with thick slices of tomato and cucumber to add color and flavor—and to help fill you up. This recipe works with the Simply Filling technique.

Tuna and White Bean Salad

PREP 20 MIN | **COOK** NONE | **SERVES** 4

- **½ cup reduced-sodium chicken broth**
- **2 teaspoons olive oil**
- **Grated zest and juice of 1 lemon**
- **½ teaspoon salt**
- **¼ teaspoon black pepper**
- **6 cups torn friseé lettuce**
- **2 different color bell peppers, chopped**
- **1 large tomato, chopped**
- **3 scallions, thinly sliced**
- **2 (6-ounce) cans water-packed solid white tuna, drained and flaked**
- **1 (15½-ounce) can cannellini (white kidney) beans, rinsed and drained**

1 To make the dressing, whisk together the broth, oil, lemon zest and juice, salt, and black pepper in a serving bowl.

2 Add the remaining ingredients to the dressing and toss to coat.

PER SERVING (generous 2 cups): 246 Cal, 4 g Fat, 1 g Sat Fat, 0 g Trans Fat, 21 mg Chol, 617 mg Sod, 28 g Carb, 8 g Fib, 27 g Prot, 121 mg Calc. *POINTS* value: *5.*

Tip

This recipe works with the Simply Filling technique.

TUNA AND WHITE BEAN SALAD

Curried Tuna Salad Platter

PREP 10 MIN | **COOK** NONE | **SERVES** 2

- **1 (6½-ounce) can water-packed solid white tuna, drained and flaked**
- **1 celery stalk, chopped**
- **2 tablespoons chopped fresh cilantro**
- **1 shallot, chopped**
- **2 tablespoons golden raisins, chopped**
- **2 tablespoons fat-free mayonnaise**
- **1 teaspoon curry powder**
- **4 red leaf lettuce leaves**
- **2 hard-cooked eggs, peeled and sliced**

1 Toss together the tuna, celery, cilantro, shallot, raisins, mayonnaise, and curry powder in a small bowl.

2 Divide the lettuce evenly between 2 plates. Mound the tuna salad evenly on the lettuce and surround with the eggs.

PER SERVING (2 lettuce leaves, ½ cup tuna salad, and 1 egg): 229 Cal, 8 g Fat, 2 g Sat Fat, 0 g Trans Fat, 243 mg Chol, 481 mg Sod, 14 g Carb, 2 g Fib, 24 g Prot, 79 mg Calc. *POINTS* value: *5.*

Filling Extra

Toss together 1 cup drained canned artichoke hearts and 1 cup sliced fresh mushrooms along with a sprinkling of lemon juice, salt, and pepper to round out this salad platter.

Tabbouleh with Shrimp

PREP 20 MIN | **COOK** NONE | **SERVES** 4

- **1¼ cups boiling water**
- **1 cup bulgur**
- **1 pound cooked peeled and devined medium shrimp, coarsely chopped**
- **1 small cucumber, peeled, seeded, and chopped**
- **2 tomatoes, cut into ½-inch pieces**
- **2 scallions, chopped**
- **½ cup chopped fresh parsley**
- **¼ cup chopped fresh mint**
- **3 tablespoons lemon juice**
- **2 teaspoons olive oil**
- **½ teaspoon salt**
- **¼ teaspoon black pepper**

1 Pour the water over the bulgur in a medium bowl. Cover and let stand until the water is absorbed, about 25 minutes. Fluff the bulgur with a fork; transfer to a serving bowl.

2 Add the remaining ingredients to the bulgur and toss to combine..

PER SERVING (about 2 cups): 246 Cal, 4 g Fat, 1 g Sat Fat, 0 g Trans Fat, 161 mg Chol, 501 mg Sod, 32 g Carb, 8 g Fib, 23 g Prot, 80 mg Calc. *POINTS* value: *4.*

Tip

This recipe works with the Simply Filling technique.

SHRIMP SALAD WITH FENNEL,
RED ONION, AND ORANGE

Shrimp Salad with Fennel, Red Onion, and Orange

PREP 20 MIN | **COOK** NONE | **SERVES** 4

- **1 tablespoon lemon juice**
- **2 teaspoons olive oil**
- **½ teaspoon salt**
- **¼ teaspoon black pepper**
- **1¼ pounds cooked peeled and deveined medium shrimp**
- **2 large navel oranges, peeled and cut into ¾-inch pieces**
- **1 fennel bulb, thinly sliced**
- **½ small red onion, thinly sliced**
- **12 pitted kalamata olives**

1 To make the dressing, whisk together the lemon juice, oil, salt, and pepper in a serving bowl.

2 Add the remaining ingredients to the dressing and toss to coat.

PER SERVING (about 2 cups): 241 Cal, 5 g Fat, 1 g Sat Fat, 0 g Trans Fat, 276 mg Chol, 759 mg Sod, 17 g Carb, 5 g Fib, 31 g Prot, 136 mg Calc. *POINTS* value: *4.*

In the Kitchen

The easiest way to thinly slice fennel is with a vegetable slicer (sometimes called a V-slicer). The blade is very sharp and the slicing thickness is adjustable. This recipe works with the Simply Filling technique.

Key West–Style Shrimp Salad

PREP 20 MIN | **COOK** NONE | **SERVES** 4

- **⅓ cup fat-free mayonnaise**
- **⅓ cup sour cream**
- **½ teaspoon salt**
- **¼ teaspoon black pepper**
- **1 pound cooked peeled and deveined medium shrimp**
- **2 cups fresh pineapple chunks**
- **2 cups strawberries, hulled and thickly sliced**
- **¼ cup thinly sliced fresh mint**
- **2 scallions, thinly sliced**
- **1 jalapeño pepper, seeded and minced**
- **4 cups mixed baby salad greens**

1 To make the dressing, whisk together the mayonnaise, sour cream, salt, and black pepper in a serving bowl.

2 Toss together the shrimp, pineapple, strawberries, mint, scallions, and jalapeño pepper in a large bowl.

3 Divide the salad greens evenly among 4 plates. Top evenly with the shrimp mixture. Serve the dressing alongside.

PER SERVING (2½ cups): 205 Cal, 2 g Fat, 1 g Sat Fat, 0 g Trans Fat, 223 mg Chol, 728 mg Sod, 22 g Carb, 5 g Fib, 26 g Prot, 105 mg Calc. *POINTS* value: 3.

Moroccan-Style Chicken

PREP 20 MIN | **MICROWAVE** 10 MIN | **SERVES** 4

- **4** **(5-ounce) skinless boneless chicken breasts, cut into 1-inch pieces**
- **2** **teaspoons canola oil**
- **1** **teaspoon ground cumin**
- **1** **teaspoon salt**
- **1** **(3-inch) cinnamon stick**
- **4** **carrots, sliced**
- **1** **red onion, chopped**
- **2** **garlic cloves, minced**
- **2** **yellow squash, diced**
- **1** **(14½-ounce) can petite diced tomatoes, drained**
- **1** **cup reduced-sodium vegetable broth**
- **1** **cup canned chickpeas, rinsed and drained**
- **¼** **cup dark raisins**

1 Stir together the chicken, 1 teaspoon of the oil, the cumin, salt, and cinnamon stick in a medium bowl.

2 Stir together the carrots, onion, garlic, and the remaining 1 teaspoon oil in a microwavable 3-quart casserole with a lid. Cover and microwave on High until the onion is softened, about 4 minutes.

3 Add the squash, tomatoes, broth, and chicken to the casserole. Cover and microwave on High until the chicken is almost cooked through, about 3 minutes, stirring once halfway through the cooking.

4 Stir in the chickpeas and raisins. Cover and microwave until the chicken is cooked through, about 2 minutes longer. Discard the cinnamon stick.

PER SERVING (1 chicken breast and about 1 cup vegetables): 365 Cal, 9 g Fat, 2 g Sat Fat, 0 g Trans Fat, 86 mg Chol, 985 mg Sod, 36 g Carb, 7 g Fib, 38 g Prot, 124 mg Calc. *POINTS* value: *7*.

Filling Extra

No Moroccan meal would be complete without a bowl of steamy hot couscous (⅔ cup cooked whole-wheat couscous per serving will increase the *POINTS* value by *2*).

Cod with Tomato-Oregano Sauce

PREP 15 MIN | **MICROWAVE** 10 MIN | **SERVES** 4

- **2 teaspoons olive oil**
- **2 scallions, chopped**
- **1 garlic clove, minced**
- **1 (14½-ounce) can diced tomatoes**
- **8 pitted kalamata olives, sliced (optional)**
- **¼ teaspoon dried oregano**
- **4 (6-ounce) cod fillets, skinned**
- **½ teaspoon salt**
- **¼ teaspoon black pepper**

1 Stir together the oil, scallions, and garlic in a large shallow glass bowl or casserole dish. Cover the bowl with plastic wrap and poke a few holes in the plastic. Microwave on High until fragrant, about 1 minute. Stir in the tomatoes, olives, if using, and oregano. Cover and microwave on High until the flavors are blended, about 3 minutes.

2 Spray a shallow microwavable dish with nonstick spray. Place the cod in the dish in one layer. Sprinkle the fish with the salt and pepper. Cover the dish with wax paper and microwave on High until the fish is just opaque in the center, about 6 minutes. Spoon the tomato sauce over the fish.

PER SERVING (1 piece cod and 5 tablespoons sauce without olives): 194 Cal, 6g Fat, 1g Sat Fat, 0g Trans Fat, 65mg Chol, 614mg Sod, 6g Carb, 1g Fib, 28g Prot, 43mg Calc. *POINTS* value: *4.*

Filling Extra

Turn this tasty fish dish into a satisfying meal by serving it with steamed green beans and a bowl of brown rice (½ cup cooked brown rice for each serving will increase the *POINTS* value by *2*). This recipe works with the Simply Filling technique.

COD WITH TOMATO-OREGANO SAUCE

Vegetarian Chili in Bread Bowls

PREP 5 MIN | **MICROWAVE** 5 MIN | **SERVES** 4

- **2 (15-ounce) cans low-sodium vegetarian chili**
- **4 (2-ounce) whole-grain rolls**
- **1 cup shredded fat-free cheddar cheese**
- **½ small red onion, chopped**
- **2 tablespoons chopped fresh cilantro**

1 Put the chili in a large microwavable bowl. Microwave on High until heated through, about 5 minutes, stirring once or twice.

2 Meanwhile, slice the top third off each roll. Pull out the soft bready center to form bread bowls. Spoon the chili evenly into the bread bowls and top evenly with the cheddar, onion, and cilantro.

PER SERVING (1 filled bowl): 311 Cal, 7 g Fat, 1 g Sat Fat, 0 g Trans Fat, 5 mg Chol, 1053 mg Sod, 45 g Carb, 9 g Fib, 19 g Prot, 309 mg Calc. *POINTS* value: *6.*

Filling Extra

Add some crunch to your meal by serving the chili with a stack of celery and carrot sticks.

Easy Garlicky Broccoli

PREP 10 MIN | **MICROWAVE** 5 MIN | **SERVES** 4

- **1 bunch broccoli, tops cut into 2-inch florets and stems sliced**
- **2 tablespoons water**
- **4 teaspoons olive oil**
- **1 large garlic clove, minced**
- **¼ teaspoon red pepper flakes**
- **¼ teaspoon salt**
- **¼ cup grated Parmesan cheese**

1 Put the broccoli in a large microwavable bowl and add the water. Cover the bowl with plastic wrap and prick a few holes in the plastic. Microwave on High until the broccoli is crisp-tender, about 3 minutes, stirring once halfway through the cooking; drain. Return the broccoli to the bowl.

2 Stir together the oil, garlic, red pepper flakes, and salt in a small microwavable bowl. Microwave on High until the garlic sizzles, about 30 seconds. Add the garlic mixture to the broccoli and toss to coat. Sprinkle with the Parmesan.

PER SERVING (about 1¼ cups): 137 Cal, 7 g Fat, 2 g Sat Fat, 0 g Trans Fat, 5 mg Chol, 341 mg Sod, 15 g Carb, 6 g Fib, 7 g Prot, 163 mg Calc. *POINTS* value: *3*.

Filling Extra

Make this a complete meal by serving the broccoli with deli roast chicken breasts and a bowl of microwave-warmed potatoes tossed with chopped parsley (1 (3-ounce) cooked skinless boneless chicken breast, and 1 cup canned potatoes per serving will increase the *POINTS* value by *4*).

PROVENÇAL-STYLE
VEGETABLE-CHICKPEA STEW

Provençal-Style Vegetable-Chickpea Stew

PREP 20 MIN | **MICROWAVE** 20 MIN | **SERVES** 4

- **1 eggplant (1 pound), cut into ¾-inch dice**
- **2 teaspoons olive oil**
- **1 (28-ounce) can fire-roasted diced tomatoes, drained**
- **3 tablespoons tomato paste**
- **2 red bell peppers, cut into ¾-inch pieces**
- **2 small zucchini, sliced**
- **1 large onion, coarsely chopped**
- **2 large garlic cloves, minced**
- **1 teaspoon dried thyme**
- **¾ teaspoon salt**
- **¼ teaspoon black pepper**
- **¼ cup chopped fresh parsley**
- **2½ cups rinsed and drained canned chickpeas**
- **¼ cup grated Parmesan cheese**

1 Stir together the eggplant and oil in a large microwavable bowl. Cover the bowl with plastic wrap and prick a few holes in the plastic. Microwave on High until the eggplant is softened, about 4 minutes.

2 Add all the remaining ingredients except the beans and Parmesan to the eggplant and stir to combine. Microwave, covered, on High until the vegetables are softened, about 15 minutes, stirring every 5 minutes. Stir in the chickpeas and let stand about 5 minutes. Serve warm or at room temperature sprinkled with the Parmesan.

PER SERVING (about 1½ cups): **342 Cal, 8 g Fat, 2 g Sat Fat, 0 g Trans Fat, 5 mg Chol, 993 mg Sod, 58 g Carb, 14 g Fib, 17 g Prot, 225 mg Calc.** *POINTS* value: *7.*

Mixed Mushroom–Roast Beef Pilaf

PREP 5 MIN | **MICROWAVE** 15 MIN | **SERVES** 4

- **1 cup quick-cooking brown rice**
- **1 red bell pepper, chopped**
- **½ cup chopped onion**
- **2 teaspoons olive oil**
- **½ teaspoon dried thyme**
- **¾ pound mixed mushrooms, sliced**
- **½ teaspoon salt**
- **⅛ teaspoon black pepper**
- **½ pound lean roast beef, trimmed and cut into strips**

1 Microwave the rice according to the package directions, omitting the fat if desired; keep warm.

2 Stir together the bell pepper, onion, oil and thyme in a large microwavable bowl. Cover the bowl with plastic wrap and prick a few holes in the plastic. Microwave on High until the bell pepper is softened, about 2 minutes.

3 Stir in all the remaining ingredients except the roast beef and microwave, covered, on High until softened, about 2 minutes. Add the roast beef and rice; stir to combine.

PER SERVING (generous 1 cup): 211 Cal, 5 g Fat, 1 g Sat Fat, 0 g Trans Fat, 28 mg Chol, 1186 mg Sod, 26 g Carb, 4 g Fib, 17 g Prot, 23 mg Calc. *POINTS* value: *4.*

Filling Extra

Enjoy this dish with microwave-cooked green beans. Put 4 cups trimmed green beans in a microwavable shallow dish and add 2 tablespoons water. Cover with a lid or plastic wrap with a few holes poked in and microwave on High until crisp-tender, about 4 minutes.

This recipe works with the Simply Filling technique.

Butternut Squash with Apricot Jam and Pecans

PREP 10 MIN | **MICROWAVE** 10 MIN | **SERVES** 4

- **1 (20-ounce) package cut up peeled butternut squash**
- **⅓ cup reduced-sodium vegetable broth**
- **2 teaspoons butter, cut into pieces**
- **3 tablespoons apricot or peach jam**
- **2 teaspoons grated peeled fresh ginger**
- **⅛ teaspoon black pepper**
- **¼ cup chopped pecans**

1 Stir together the squash, broth, and butter in a large microwavable casserole dish or bowl. Cover the dish with plastic wrap and prick a few holes in the plastic. Microwave on High until the squash is tender, about 9 minutes, stirring once halfway through the cooking.

2 Stir in the jam, ginger, and pepper; microwave, covered, on High until heated through, about 1 minute. Sprinkle with the pecans.

PER SERVING (1 cup): 157 Cal, 7 g Fat, 2 g Sat Fat, 0 g Trans Fat, 5 mg Chol, 45 mg Sod, 25 g Carb, 3 g Fib, 2 g Prot, 60 mg Calc. *POINTS* value *3.*

Filling Extra

Accompany the squash with Canadian bacon, cooked according to package directions, and a bowl of your favorite microwave-cooked leafy green (3 slices of Canadian bacon per serving will increase the *POINTS* value by *3*).

chapter 4

super-hungry specials

When you are famished, turn to these dishes

BEEF-BARLEY STEW WITH
ROASTED VEGETABLES

Beef-Barley Stew with Roasted Vegetables

PREP 30 MIN | **COOK** 1 HR 15 MIN | **SERVES** 8

- **1 celery root, peeled and cut into chunks**
- **4 carrots, cut into chunks**
- **2 parsnips, cut into chunks**
- **2 onions, chopped**
- **1 tablespoon chopped fresh thyme**
- **1½ pounds boneless lean beef chuck, cut into 1-inch chunks**
- **6 cups reduced-sodium beef broth**
- **3 garlic cloves, chopped**
- **½ teaspoon salt**
- **¼ teaspoon black pepper**
- **1 (8-ounce) package sliced cremini mushrooms**
- **1 cup pearl barley, rinsed**

1 Preheat the oven to 450°F and spray a large shallow roasting pan with nonstick spray.

2 Put the celery root, carrots, parsnips, onions, and thyme in the pan and spray with nonstick spray; toss to coat. Roast, stirring occasionally, until the vegetables are browned and crisp-tender, about 30 minutes.

3 Meanwhile, spray a Dutch oven with nonstick spray and place over medium-high heat. Cook the beef, in batches, until browned on all sides, about 4 minutes. Transfer the beef to a plate.

4 Return the beef to the pot. Add 5½ cups of the broth, the garlic, salt, and pepper; bring to a boil. Reduce the heat and simmer, covered, 45 minutes.

5 Stir in the mushrooms and barley and bring to a boil. Reduce the heat and simmer, covered, stirring occasionally, 15 minutes. Stir in the roasted vegetables and bring to a boil. Reduce the heat and simmer, covered, until the beef is fork-tender and the barley is tender, about 15 minutes, adding the remaining ½ cup broth if the stew seems too thick.

PER SERVING (generous 1 cup): 318 Cal, 11 g Fat, 4 g Sat Fat, 0 g Trans Fat, 44 mg Chol, 366 mg Sod, 35 g Carb, 7 g Fib, 22 g Prot, 61 mg Calc. *POINTS* value: *6.*

Filling Extra

Steam a bunch of red Swiss chard, coarsely chopped, and serve with stew.

Cuban-Style Shredded Beef and Rice

PREP 20 MIN | **COOK** 1 HR 15 MIN | **SERVES** 4

- **1 (1-pound) flank steak, trimmed**
- **1 (14½-ounce) can reduced-sodium beef broth**
- **3 garlic cloves, peeled + 2 garlic cloves, minced**
- **1 teaspoon olive oil**
- **1 onion, chopped**
- **1 (14½-ounce) can diced tomatoes**
- **1 jalapeño pepper, seeded and minced**
- **1 teaspoon dried oregano**
- **1 teaspoon ground cumin**
- **½ teaspoon salt**
- **¼ cup chopped fresh cilantro**
- **4 cups hot cooked brown rice**
- **Lime wedges**

1 Combine the steak, broth, and peeled garlic in a medium nonstick skillet and bring to a boil over high heat. Reduce the heat and simmer, covered, until the steak is very tender, about 1 hour.

2 Remove the skillet from the heat and let stand 15 minutes. Reserve ½ cup of the broth; save the remaining broth for another use. Discard the garlic. Transfer the steak to a cutting board; with 2 forks, shred the beef.

3 Wipe out the skillet. Add the oil and set over medium-high heat. Add the onion and minced garlic and cook, stirring occasionally, until the onion is slightly softened, about 4 minutes. Stir in the tomatoes, jalapeño pepper, oregano, cumin, and salt; cook, stirring, 5 minutes longer. Stir in the shredded beef and the reserved ½ cup broth. Continue to cook until most of the liquid is evaporated, about 3 minutes.

4 Remove the skillet from the heat and stir in the cilantro. Serve with the rice and lime wedges.

PER SERVING (¾ cup beef mixture and 1 cup rice): 466 Cal, 8 g Fat, 2 g Sat Fat, 0 g Trans Fat, 83 mg Chol, 1112 mg Sod, 55 g Carb, 9 g Fib, 42 g Prot, 85 mg Calc. *POINTS* value: *9.*

In the Kitchen

This dish is based on the Cuban classic ropa vieja (ROH-pah vee-EH-ha), which means "old clothes" in Spanish and refers to the ragged appearance of this delicious shredded beef. It's typically served over rice, but you can also use it as a super-flavorful filling for tacos, burritos, or enchiladas. This recipe works with the Simply Filling technique.

Rosemary Chicken Thighs with Roast Potatoes

PREP 15 MIN | **ROAST** 30 MIN | **SERVES** 4

- **4 (¼-pound) skinless boneless chicken thighs, trimmed**
- **2 teaspoons olive oil**
- **2 garlic cloves, minced**
- **1 teaspoon grated lemon zest**
- **1 tablespoon lemon juice**
- **1½ teaspoons dried rosemary**
- **1 teaspoon dried thyme**
- **¾ teaspoon salt**
- **6 small new potatoes, scrubbed and quartered**

1 Combine the chicken, 1 teaspoon of the oil, the garlic, lemon zest and juice, rosemary, thyme, and ½ teaspoon of the salt in a large zip-close plastic bag. Squeeze out the air and seal the bag; turn to coat the chicken. Refrigerate, turning the bag occasionally, at least 30 minutes or up to overnight.

2 Toss together the potatoes and the remaining 1 teaspoon oil and ¼ teaspoon salt in a medium bowl. Spray a baking sheet with nonstick spray and spread the potatoes on the baking sheet. Place the potatoes in the oven and turn the oven on to 425°F. When the temperature reaches 425°F, remove the potatoes from the oven. Toss the potatoes, then push them to one side of the pan.

3 Remove the chicken from the marinade and place on the baking sheet. Discard the marinade. Roast until the chicken is cooked through and the potatoes are tender and browned, about 20 minutes.

PER SERVING (1 piece chicken and ½ cup potatoes): 273 Cal, 11 g Fat, 3 g Sat Fat, 0 g Trans Fat, 71 mg Chol, 512 mg Sod, 16 g Carb, 2 g Fib, 25 g Prot, 57 mg Calc. ***POINTS* value: *6*.**

Filling Extra

Toss 2 carrots, cut into 1-inch chunks, in with the potatoes to get more delicious roasted vegetables. This recipe works with the Simply Filling technique.

Pepper Steak Heroes

PREP 10 MIN | **COOK** 15 MIN | **SERVES** 4

- **3 assorted color bell peppers, sliced**
- **1 large Spanish onion, thinly sliced**
- **2 garlic cloves, finely chopped**
- **½ teaspoon salt**
- **¼ teaspoon black pepper**
- **4 (¼-pound) beef cube steaks**
- **4 (2-ounce) whole-wheat hero rolls, split and toasted**

1 Spray a large nonstick skillet with nonstick spray and set over medium-high heat. Add the bell peppers and cook, stirring frequently, until crisp-tender, about 3 minutes. Add the onion, garlic, salt, and black pepper; cook until the vegetables are lightly browned and softened, about 8 minutes longer. Transfer the vegetable mixture to a bowl and keep warm.

2 Wipe out the skillet. Spray the skillet with nonstick spray and set over medium-high heat. Add the steaks and cook until browned and cooked through, about 2 minutes on each side.

3 Place 1 steak in each roll and top with the bell pepper mixture.

PER SERVING (1 hero sandwich): 323 Cal, 6 g Fat, 2 g Sat Fat, 1 g Trans Fat, 59 mg Chol, 595 mg Sod, 39 g Carb, 7 g Fib, 30 g Prot, 83 mg Calc. *POINTS* value: *6.*

Spaghetti with Quick Bolognese Sauce

PREP 10 MIN | **COOK** 20 MIN | **SERVES** 4

- **1 pound ground lean beef (7% fat or less)**
- **1 onion, chopped**
- **1 green bell pepper, chopped**
- **2 garlic cloves, minced**
- **1 (28-ounce) can diced tomatoes**
- **2 teaspoons dried basil**
- **¼ teaspoon salt**
- **Pinch red pepper flakes**
- **8 ounces whole-wheat spaghetti**

1 Spray a large nonstick skillet with nonstick spray and set over medium-high heat. Add the beef and cook, breaking it apart with a wooden spoon, until lightly browned, about 4 minutes. Stir in the onion, bell pepper, and garlic; cook, stirring occasionally, until the vegetables are softened, about 5 minutes. Stir in the tomatoes, basil, salt, and red pepper flakes; bring the mixture to a boil. Reduce the heat and simmer, stirring occasionally, until slightly thickened, about 10 minutes.

2 Meanwhile, cook the spaghetti according to the package directions, omitting the salt if desired. Drain.

3 Toss the pasta with the sauce.

PER SERVING (1½ cups spaghetti and sauce): 413 Cal, 8 g Fat, 3 g Sat Fat, 0 g Trans Fat, 64 mg Chol, 693 mg Sod, 56 g Carb, 8 g Fib, 33 g Prot, 114 mg Calc. *POINTS* **value:** *8.*

Tip

This recipe works with the Simply Filling technique.

Apricot and Mustard–Glazed Pork Roast

PREP 10 MIN | **ROAST** 40 MIN | **SERVES** 4

- **3** **garlic cloves, minced**
- **1** **tablespoon chopped fresh rosemary or 1 teaspoon dried**
- **¾** **teaspoon salt**
- **¼** **teaspoon black pepper**
- **1** **(1¼-pound) boneless center-cut pork loin roast, trimmed**
- **2** **tablespoons apricot jam**
- **2** **tablespoons Dijon mustard**

1 Preheat the oven to 400°F. Lightly spray a roasting pan with nonstick spray.

2 Stir together the garlic, rosemary, salt, and pepper in a small bowl. Rub the mixture over the pork. Place the pork in the prepared pan and roast 30 minutes.

3 Stir together the jam and mustard in a small bowl and brush all over the pork. Continue to roast the pork until an instant-read thermometer inserted into the center registers 160°F for medium, about 10 minutes longer. Transfer to a cutting board and let stand 10 minutes. Cut the roast into 12 slices.

PER SERVING (3 slices pork): 237 Cal, 10 g Fat, 3 g Sat Fat, 0 g Trans Fat, 79 mg Chol, 696 mg Sod, 8 g Carb, 0 g Fib, 28 g Prot, 46 mg Calc. *POINTS* value: *6.*

Filling Extra

Toss 1 pound of scrubbed baby or halved fingerling potatoes with a little rosemary, salt, and pepper, and lightly spray with nonstick spray. Scatter in the roasting pan around the pork and roast until tender. This will increase the per-serving *POINTS* value by *1.*

APRICOT AND MUSTARD–GLAZED PORK ROAST

Lechón Asado (Citrus-Marinated Roast Pork)

PREP 10 MIN | **ROAST** 40 MIN | **SERVES** 8

- **¼ cup finely chopped onion**
- **6 garlic cloves, minced**
- **⅓ cup orange juice**
- **3 tablespoons lime juice**
- **1 tablespoon olive oil**
- **1 teaspoon dried oregano**
- **1 teaspoon ground cumin**
- **¼ teaspoon red pepper flakes**
- **1 (2-pound) boneless center-cut pork loin roast, trimmed**
- **1 teaspoon salt**
- **¼ teaspoon black pepper**
- **12 carrots, cut into 2-inch chunks**

1 Combine the onion, garlic, orange juice, lime juice, oil, oregano, cumin, and red pepper flakes in a large zip-close plastic bag. Add the pork to the bag. Squeeze out the air and seal the bag; turn to coat the pork. Refrigerate, turning the bag occasionally, about 3 hours.

2 Preheat the oven to 425°F. Place a rack in a large roasting pan and spray the rack with nonstick spray.

3 Remove the pork from the plastic bag and place on the rack. Discard the marinade. Sprinkle the pork with the salt and black pepper. Spray the carrots with olive oil nonstick spray and scatter around the pork. Roast until an instant-read thermometer inserted into the center of the pork registers 160°F for medium and the carrots are tender, about 40 minutes.

4 Transfer the pork to a cutting board and let stand 10 minutes. Cut the pork into 16 slices and serve with the carrots.

PER SERVING (2 slices pork and about ⅔ cup carrots): 252 Cal, 11 g Fat, 3 g Sat Fat, 0 g Trans Fat, 72 mg Chol, 404 mg Sod, 12 g Carb, 3 g Fib, 26 g Prot, 47 mg Calc. *POINTS* value: *6.*

Filling Extra

Round out your meal with baked potatoes (1 large baked potato per serving will increase the *POINTS* value by *3*).

Cajun-Spiced Roast Pork

PREP 5 MIN | **COOK/ROAST** 25 MIN | **SERVES** 4

- **1 tablespoon paprika**
- **½ teaspoon ground cumin**
- **½ teaspoon sugar**
- **½ teaspoon salt**
- **⅛ teaspoon cayenne**
- **1 (1-pound) pork tenderloin, trimmed**

1 Preheat the oven to 400°F.

2 On a sheet of wax paper, combine the paprika, cumin, sugar, salt, and cayenne. Roll the pork in the mixture until evenly coated.

3 Spray a large ovenproof skillet with nonstick spray and set over medium-high heat. Tuck the thin end of the tenderloin under so it is an even thickness and place in the skillet. Cook until lightly browned on all sides, about 5 minutes.

4 Transfer the skillet to the oven and roast until an instant-read thermometer inserted into the center of the tenderloin registers 160°F for medium, about 20 minutes.

5 Transfer the pork to a cutting board and let stand 10 minutes. Cut into 16 slices.

PER SERVING (4 slices pork): 139 Cal, 4 g Fat, 1 g Sat Fat, 0 g Trans Fat, 63 mg Chol, 337 mg Sod, 2 g Carb, 0 g Fib, 23 g Prot, 10 mg Calc. *POINTS* value: *3*.

Filling Extra

Baked sweet potatoes are the perfect counterpoint to the spicy pork (1 large baked sweet potato per serving will increase the *POINTS* value by *3*).

SAUCY PAN-ROASTED
PORK CHOPS
OVER PASTA

Saucy Pan-Roasted Pork Chops over Pasta

PREP 15 MIN | **COOK** 30 MIN | **SERVES** 4

- **4 ounces whole-wheat ziti or penne**
- **2 garlic cloves, minced**
- **1 (14½-ounce) can tomato puree**
- **¾ teaspoon Italian seasoning**
- **Pinch red pepper flakes**
- **4 (5-ounce) bone-in pork rib or loin chops, trimmed**
- **½ teaspoon salt**
- **¼ teaspoon black pepper**
- **¼ cup shredded fat-free mozzarella cheese**
- **Small fresh basil leaves (optional)**

1 Cook the ziti according to the package directions, omitting the salt if desired.

2 Meanwhile, spray a large saucepan with olive oil cooking spray and set over medium heat. Add the garlic and cook, stirring, until fragrant, about 20 seconds. Add the tomato puree, Italian seasoning, and red pepper flakes and bring to a boil; reduce the heat and simmer, stirring occasionally, 10 minutes.

3 Generously spray a large skillet with nonstick spray and set over high heat. Sprinkle the pork with the salt and black pepper. Add the chops to the skillet and cook until lightly browned, about 2 minutes on each side. Reduce the heat to medium-low and sprinkle the chops evenly with the mozzarella. Cover the skillet and cook until the cheese is melted and an instant-read thermometer inserted into the side of a chop registers 160°F for medium, about 6 minutes.

4 Divide the ziti evenly among 4 plates and top with the tomato sauce and a pork chop. Sprinkle with basil, if using.

PER SERVING (1 cup ziti, 1 pork chop, and scant ½ cup sauce): 357 Cal, 11 g Fat, 4 g Sat Fat, 0 g Trans Fat, 75 mg Chol, 933 mg Sod, 33 g Carb, 4 g Fib, 34 g Prot, 108 mg Calc. ***POINTS*** **value:** ***7.***

Filling Extra

Complete this robust meal by serving steamed spinach alongside. This recipe works with the Simply Filling technique.

Ham with Apples and Mustard

PREP 10 MIN | **COOK** 20 MIN | **SERVES** 4

- **4** **(¼-pound) slices reduced-sodium lean deli ham, trimmed**
- **1** **small onion, chopped**
- **3** **red apples, cored and cut into ½-inch wedges**
- **1½** **cups apple cider**
- **2** **teaspoons Dijon mustard**
- **1** **tablespoon cornstarch**
- **2** **tablespoons cold water**

1 Spray a large nonstick skillet with nonstick spray and set over high heat. Add the ham and cook until lightly browned, about 2 minutes on each side. Transfer to a plate.

2 Add the onion to the skillet and cook over medium heat, stirring frequently, until softened, about 5 minutes. Add the apples, cider, and mustard; cook, stirring frequently, until the apples are tender, about 5 minutes longer.

3 Stir together the cornstarch and water in a cup until smooth, then add to the skillet. Cook, stirring constantly, until the sauce thickens and bubbles, about 2 minutes. Return the ham steaks to the skillet and cook until heated through, about 1 minute longer.

PER SERVING (1 slice ham and about ½ cup apple with sauce): 261 Cal, 6 g Fat, 2 g Sat Fat, 0 g Trans Fat, 53 mg Chol, 1045 mg Sod, 30 g Carb, 3 g Fib, 22 g Prot, 27 mg Calc. *POINTS* value: *5*.

Filling Extra

Give this tasty meal some Southern style by serving it with corn grits (1 cup cooked corn grits per serving will increase the ***POINTS*** value by *3*).

Minted Lamb Chops with Lemony Bulgur

PREP 10 MIN | **BROIL** 10 MIN | **SERVES** 4

- **4 (¼-pound) boneless lamb loin chops, trimmed**
- **2 tablespoons chopped fresh mint**
- **2 garlic cloves, minced**
- **2 teaspoons olive oil**
- **½ teaspoon salt**
- **1 cup bulgur**
- **1 large tomato, coarsely chopped**
- **Grated zest and juice of 1 lemon**
- **2 tablespoons chopped fresh mint**
- **2 tablespoons chopped fresh chives**

1 Combine the lamb, mint, garlic, oil, and salt in a large zip-close plastic bag. Squeeze out the air and seal the bag; turn to coat the lamb. Refrigerate at least 20 minutes or up to overnight.

2 Spray the broiler rack with nonstick spray and preheat the broiler. Remove the lamb from the marinade and place the lamb chops on the broiler rack. Discard the marinade. Broil 5 inches from the heat until an instant-read thermometer inserted into the side of a chop registers 145°F for medium-rare, about 5 minutes on each side.

3 Meanwhile, prepare the bulgur according to the package directions, omitting the salt if desired. Add the remaining ingredients and toss to coat. Serve with the lamb.

PER SERVING (1 lamb chop and ¾ cup bulgur): 319 Cal, 10 g Fat, 3 g Sat Fat, 0 g Trans Fat, 74 mg Chol, 367 mg Sod, 30 g Carb, 7 g Fib, 29 g Prot, 37 mg Calc. *POINTS* value: *6.*

Tip

This recipe works with the Simply Filling technique.

Grilled Lamb Chops and Asparagus with Garlic Mayonnaise

PREP 10 MIN | **COOK/GRILL** 20 MIN | **SERVES** 4

- **½ teaspoon olive oil**
- **4 small garlic cloves, unpeeled**
- **¼ cup fat-free mayonnaise**
- **1 teaspoon grated lemon zest**
- **1 teaspoon lemon juice**
- **4 (5-ounce) lamb loin chops, about 1 inch thick, trimmed**
- **1 pound thick asparagus spears, trimmed**
- **1½ teaspoons salt**
- **½ teaspoon black pepper**

1 Spray the grill rack with nonstick spray. Preheat the grill to medium-high or prepare a medium-high fire using the direct method.

2 Put the oil and garlic in a small nonstick skillet and set over medium-low heat. Cook, turning the garlic occasionally, until golden and softened, about 8 minutes.

3 Transfer the garlic to a serving dish. When cool enough to handle, peel the garlic and mash with a fork. Stir in the mayonnaise and lemon zest and juice.

4 Sprinkle the lamb and asparagus with the salt and pepper. Spray the asparagus with olive oil nonstick spray. Place the lamb and asparagus on the grill rack. Grill until an instant-read thermometer inserted into the center of a chop registers 145°F for medium-rare, about 4 minutes on each side, and the asparagus is browned in spots and just tender, about 8 minutes. Serve with the garlic mayonnaise.

PER SERVING (1 lamb chop, about 5 asparagus spears, and 1 tablespoon mayonnaise): 260 Cal, 11 g Fat, 4 g Sat Fat, 0 g Trans Fat, 94 mg Chol, 1079 mg Sod, 8 g Carb, 3 g Fib, 31 g Prot, 44 mg Calc. *POINTS* value: *6.*

Tip

This recipe works with the Simply Filling technique.

Best-Ever Country Captain Chicken

PREP 20 MIN | **COOK** 30 MIN | **SERVES** 4

- **2 teaspoons canola oil**
- **1¼ pounds skinless boneless chicken breasts, cut into 1-inch pieces**
- **1 large onion, chopped**
- **1 Granny Smith apple, peeled, cored, and diced**
- **1 green bell pepper, chopped**
- **1 tablespoon minced garlic**
- **1 tablespoon minced peeled fresh ginger**
- **1 tablespoon Madras curry powder**
- **¼ teaspoon cinnamon**
- **¼ teaspoon salt**
- **1 (14½-ounce) can diced tomatoes**
- **1 cup reduced-sodium chicken broth**
- **¼ cup dark raisins**
- **1 tablespoon sliced or slivered almonds, toasted**

1 Heat 1 teaspoon of the oil in a nonstick Dutch oven or large pot over medium-high heat. Add the chicken and cook, turning occasionally, until browned, about 6 minutes. Transfer to a plate.

2 Add the remaining 1 teaspoon oil to the Dutch oven and reduce the heat to medium. Add the onion, apple, bell pepper, garlic, and ginger; cook, stirring, until the vegetables are softened, about 5 minutes. Stir in the curry powder, cinnamon, and salt; cook, stirring, 1 minute longer.

3 Return the chicken to the Dutch oven along with the tomatoes, broth, and raisins; bring to a boil. Reduce the heat and simmer, covered, until the chicken is cooked through and the flavors are blended, about 15 minutes. Serve sprinkled with the almonds.

PER SERVING (about 1½ cups stew): 309 Cal, 8 g Fat, 2 g Sat Fat, 0 g Trans Fat, 86 mg Chol, 516 mg Sod, 24 g Carb, 4 g Fib, 35 g Prot, 90 mg Calc. *POINTS* value: *6.*

In the Kitchen

Toasting almonds enhances their flavor and texture. Place the almonds in a small heavy skillet and set the skillet over medium heat. Cook, shaking the pan frequently, until lightly browned, about 5 minutes. Immediately transfer the almonds to a plate to cool or they will continue to brown.

CACCIATORE-STYLE CHICKEN AND VEGETABLES

Cacciatore-Style Chicken and Vegetables

PREP 20 MIN | **COOK** 35 MIN | **SERVES** 6

- **3 pounds bone-in chicken breasts and thighs, skin removed**
- **½ teaspoon salt**
- **¼ teaspoon black pepper**
- **1 tablespoon olive oil**
- **2 red bell peppers, thinly sliced**
- **1 (8-ounce) package sliced cremini mushrooms**
- **1 celery stalk, thinly sliced**
- **1 carrot, thinly sliced**
- **1 red onion, sliced**
- **3 garlic cloves, minced**
- **2 teaspoons chopped fresh rosemary**
- **2 cups fat-free marinara sauce**

1 Sprinkle the chicken with the salt and black pepper.

2 Heat 2 teaspoons of the oil in a nonstick Dutch oven over medium-high heat. Add the chicken, in batches, and cook until browned, about 4 minutes on each side. Transfer the chicken to a plate and set aside.

3 Add the remaining 1 teaspoon oil to the Dutch oven. Add the bell peppers, mushrooms, celery, carrot, onion, garlic, and rosemary; cook, stirring, until the vegetables are slightly softened, about 3 minutes.

4 Return the chicken to the Dutch oven. Add the marinara sauce and bring to a simmer. Reduce the heat and simmer, covered, until the chicken is cooked through and the vegetables are tender, about 20 minutes.

PER SERVING (1 piece chicken and ¾ cup vegetables with sauce): 296 Cal, 11 g Fat, 3 g Sat Fat, 0 g Trans Fat, 95 mg Chol, 635 mg Sod, 12 g Carb, 3 g Fib, 36 g Prot, 69 mg Calc. *POINTS* value: *6.*

Chicken and Vegetable Ragu with Herb Dumplings

PREP 15 MIN | **COOK** 40 MIN | **SERVES** 4

- **1 pound skinless boneless chicken breasts, cut into 1-inch pieces**
- **¾ teaspoon salt**
- **¼ teaspoon black pepper**
- **1 onion, chopped**
- **1 tablespoon + ½ cup all-purpose flour**
- **2 cups reduced-sodium chicken broth**
- **2 (5-ounce) red potatoes, scrubbed and diced**
- **¼ cup whole-wheat flour**
- **1½ teaspoons baking powder**
- **½ cup fat-free milk**
- **2 teaspoons unsalted butter, melted**
- **2 tablespoons chopped fresh parsley**
- **2 tablespoons chopped fresh chives**
- **1½ cups frozen mixed peas and carrots, thawed**
- **1 teaspoon dried thyme**

1 Spray a nonstick Dutch oven with nonstick spray and set over medium-high heat. Add the chicken and sprinkle with ¼ teaspoon of the salt, and the pepper. Cook, stirring occasionally, until the chicken is lightly browned, about 6 minutes. Add the onion and cook, stirring, until softened, about 5 minutes longer.

2 Stir in 1 tablespoon of the flour and cook, stirring constantly, 1 minute. Stir in the broth and potatoes and bring to a boil. Reduce the heat and simmer, covered, until the potatoes are tender, about 15 minutes.

3 Meanwhile, to make the dumpling dough, whisk together the remaining ½ cup all-purpose flour, the whole-wheat flour, baking powder, and the remaining ½ teaspoon salt in a medium bowl. Add the milk, butter, parsley, and chives; stir just until a soft dough forms. Set the dumpling dough aside.

4 Stir the peas and carrots and thyme into the Dutch oven and simmer 2 minutes. Drop 8 rounded tablespoonfuls of the dumpling dough onto the surface of the simmering stew. Simmer, covered, 8 minutes. Uncover and simmer until the dumplings are doubled in size and cooked through, about 3 minutes longer.

PER SERVING (1 cup stew and 2 dumplings): 390 Cal, 7 g Fat, 3 g Sat Fat, 0 g Trans Fat, 74 mg Chol, 1207 mg Sod, 47 g Carb, 6 g Fib, 35 g Prot, 211 mg Calc. *POINTS* **value:** *8.*

Chicken and Rice with Artichoke Hearts

PREP 15 MIN | **COOK** 40 MIN | **SERVES** 4

- **2 teaspoons olive oil**
- **4 (5-ounce) skinless bone-in chicken thighs, trimmed**
- **½ teaspoon dried oregano**
- **½ teaspoon salt**
- **¼ teaspoon black pepper**
- **2 red bell peppers, chopped**
- **1 onion, chopped**
- **3 garlic cloves, minced**
- **1 cup brown rice**
- **1 (14½-ounce) can diced tomatoes**
- **1 cup water**
- **1 cup frozen artichoke hearts, thawed and coarsely chopped**
- **1 tablespoon capers, drained**

1 Heat 1 teaspoon of the oil in a large nonstick skillet over medium-high heat. Sprinkle the chicken with the oregano, ¼ teaspoon of the salt, and the black pepper. Add the chicken to the skillet and cook until browned, about 3 minutes on each side. Transfer to a plate.

2 Add the remaining 1 teaspoon oil to the skillet. Add the bell peppers, onion, and garlic; cook, stirring frequently, until the vegetables begin to soften, about 4 minutes. Add the rice and cook, stirring, 1 minute longer. Add the tomatoes, water, and the remaining ¼ teaspoon salt; bring to a boil. Reduce the heat and simmer, covered, until the rice is tender, the liquid is absorbed, and the chicken is cooked through, about 20 minutes longer.

3 Uncover the pan and scatter the artichokes and capers over the rice. Cook, covered, just until the artichokes are heated through, about 3 minutes.

PER SERVING (1 chicken thigh and 1⅓ cups rice mixture): 422 Cal, 10 g Fat, 3 g Sat Fat, 0 g Trans Fat, 57 mg Chol, 602 mg Sod, 56 g Carb, 6 g Fib, 27 g Prot, 106 mg Calc. *POINTS* value: *8.*

Tip

This recipe works with the Simply Filling technique.

Spaghetti with Fresh Tomato Sauce and Meatballs

PREP 20 MIN | **COOK** 20 MIN | **SERVES** 4

- **8 ounces whole-wheat spaghetti**
- **1 pound ground skinless turkey breast**
- **1 large egg white**
- **1 tablespoon cornmeal**
- **1 teaspoon dried oregano**
- **½ teaspoon salt**
- **¼ teaspoon sugar**
- **1 tablespoon olive oil**
- **2 garlic cloves**
- **8 plum tomatoes, chopped**
- **1 teaspoon dried basil**
- **Pinch red pepper flakes**
- **Shredded Parmesan cheese (optional)**

1 Cook the spaghetti according to the package directions, omitting the salt if desired. Drain and keep warm.

2 Meanwhile, mix together the turkey, egg white, cornmeal, oregano, ¼ teaspoon of the salt and the sugar in a large bowl. With damp hands, shape the mixture into 24 meatballs.

3 Heat 2 teaspoons of the oil in a large nonstick skillet over medium-high heat. Cook the meatballs, in batches, turning often, until browned, about 4 minutes. Transfer to a plate.

4 To make the sauce, wipe out the skillet and set over medium-high heat. Add the remaining 1 teaspoon oil and the garlic. Cook, stirring, until the garlic is fragrant, about 30 seconds. Add the tomatoes, basil, the remaining ¼ teaspoon salt, and the red pepper flakes; cook, stirring frequently, until the tomatoes are softened, about 5 minutes. Return the meatballs to the skillet and simmer, covered, until cooked through, about 5 minutes longer.

5 Divide the pasta evenly among 4 large bowls and top with the meatballs and sauce. Sprinkle with Parmesan, if using.

PER SERVING (1 cup spaghetti, 6 meatballs, and 1 cup sauce without Parmesan): 392 Cal, 6 g Fat, 1 g Sat Fat, 0 g Trans Fat, 75 mg Chol, 574 mg Sod, 51 g Carb, 6 g Fib, 37 g Prot, 60 mg Calc. *POINTS* value: *8*.

In the Kitchen

Wondering why there's cornmeal in these meatballs? Like bread or bread crumbs, it acts as a both a binder, keeping your meatballs together, and a sponge, absorbing liquid to make them light and tender. If you don't have cornmeal, you can substitute 1 tablespoon plain dried bread crumbs.

SPAGHETTI WITH
FRESH TOMATO SAUCE
AND MEATBALLS

CHICKEN WITH MUSHROOMS
AND WHITE WINE

Chicken with Mushrooms and White Wine

PREP 15 MIN | **COOK** 45 MIN | **SERVES** 4

- **4 (5-ounce) skinless boneless chicken breasts**
- **½ teaspoon salt**
- **¼ teaspoon black pepper**
- **2 teaspoons olive oil**
- **¼ pound mixed mushrooms, halved**
- **1 onion, chopped**
- **1 carrot, chopped**
- **1 celery stalk, chopped**
- **3 garlic cloves, minced**
- **1 teaspoon herbes de Provence**
- **1 tablespoon all-purpose flour**
- **1 cup reduced-sodium chicken broth**
- **¾ cup dry white wine**
- **2 tablespoons chopped fresh parsley (optional)**
- **4 cups hot cooked whole-wheat fettuccine**

1 Sprinkle the chicken with the salt and pepper. Heat 1 teaspoon of the oil in a large nonstick skillet over medium-high heat. Add the chicken and cook, turning occasionally, until browned, about 7 minutes. Transfer to a plate.

2 Add the remaining 1 teaspoon oil and the mushrooms to the skillet. Cook, stirring frequently, until the mushrooms are browned, about 5 minutes. Stir in the onion, carrot, celery, garlic, and herbes de Provence. Cook just until the onion is softened, about 3 minutes; sprinkle with the flour. Cook, stirring constantly, 1 minute longer. Add the broth and wine and bring to a boil.

3 Return the chicken and any accumulated juices to the skillet. Reduce the heat and simmer, covered, until the chicken is cooked through, about 20 minutes. Sprinkle with the parsley, if using. Serve with the pasta.

PER SERVING (1 chicken breast, ⅔ cup sauce with vegetables, and 1 cup pasta): 456 Cal, 8 g Fat, 2 g Sat Fat, 0 g Trans Fat, 92 mg Chol, 745 mg Sod, 52 g Carb, 6 g Fib, 44 g Prot, 74 mg Calc. *POINTS* value: *9*.

Filling Extra

Add 1½ cups thawed frozen pearl onions to the stew when you return the chicken to the skillet; you'll get portions that are about ⅓ cup larger for each person.

Turkey Cutlets Milanese

PREP 20 MIN | **COOK** 10 MIN | **SERVES** 4

- **8 cups baby romaine**
- **1 cup cherry tomatoes, preferably yellow, halved**
- **3 tablespoons fat-free balsamic dressing**
- **½ teaspoon salt**
- **½ teaspoon black pepper**
- **1 large egg white**
- **1 tablespoon lemon juice**
- **¼ cup yellow cornmeal**
- **2 tablespoons grated Parmesan cheese**
- **4 (¼-pound) turkey breast cutlets**
- **4 teaspoons olive oil**

1 Toss together the romaine, tomatoes, dressing, ¼ teaspoon of the salt, and ¼ teaspoon of the pepper in a large bowl; set aside.

2 Whisk together the egg white and lemon juice in a large shallow bowl or pie plate. Mix together the cornmeal, Parmesan, and the remaining ¼ teaspoon salt and ¼ teaspoon pepper on a sheet of wax paper.

3 Dip each cutlet into the egg white mixture, then coat with the cornmeal mixture, pressing lightly so it adheres.

4 Heat the oil in a large nonstick skillet over medium-high heat. Add the cutlets, in batches if necessary, and cook until browned and cooked through, about 3 minutes on each side.

5 Transfer 1 cutlet to each of 4 plates. Top evenly with the salad.

PER SERVING (1 turkey cutlet and about 1½ cups salad): 251 Cal, 7 g Fat, 2 g Sat Fat, 0 g Trans Fat, 77 mg Chol, 570 mg Sod, 15 g Carb, 3 g Fib, 31 g Prot, 116 mg Calc. *POINTS* value: *5.*

Filling Extra

Serve this ever-popular Italian entrée with a bowl of whole-wheat capellini lightly sprayed with olive oil nonstick spray and sprinkle with grated lemon zest (1 cup cooked whole-wheat capellini will increase the per-serving *POINTS* value by *3*).

Baked Ziti with Summer Squash

PREP 10 MIN | **COOK/BAKE** 30 MIN | **SERVES** 5

- **2 cups whole-wheat ziti or penne**
- **2 teaspoons olive oil**
- **1 yellow squash, thinly sliced**
- **1 small zucchini, thinly sliced**
- **2 garlic cloves, minced**
- **2 cups marinara sauce**
- **2 cups fat-free ricotta cheese**
- **1 cup shredded fat-free mozzarella cheese**

1 Cook the ziti according to the package directions, omitting the salt if desired. Drain.

2 Meanwhile, preheat the oven to 375°F. Spray an 8-inch square baking dish with nonstick spray.

3 Heat the oil in a large nonstick skillet over medium heat. Add the squash, zucchini, and garlic; cook, stirring, until softened, about 6 minutes. Stir in the cooked ziti and the marinara sauce.

4 Transfer the mixture to the prepared baking dish and top evenly with the ricotta and mozzarella. Bake until heated through and bubbling, about 20 minutes.

PER SERVING (generous 1½ cups): 370 Cal, 6 g Fat, 1 g Sat Fat, 0 g Trans Fat, 13 mg Chol, 956 mg Sod, 55 g Carb, 5 g Fib, 26 g Prot, 409 mg Calc. *POINTS* value: *7.*

chapter 5

no-fuss suppers

Just 15 minutes—or less—to prepare these favorites

Maple and Chili–Broiled T-Bone Steak

PREP 5 MIN | **BROIL** 10 MIN | **SERVES** 6

1 canned chipotle en adobo, minced
2 tablespoons maple syrup
2 garlic cloves, minced
Grated zest of ½ orange
1 teaspoon salt
1 teaspoon chili powder
1 teaspoon ground cumin
1 teaspoon onion powder
1 (1½- to 1¾-pound) T-bone steak, 1 inch thick, trimmed

1 To make the rub, stir together all the ingredients except the steak in a small bowl. Rub the chipotle mixture on both sides of the steak. Put the steak on a plate; cover and refrigerate at least 1 hour or up to 6 hours.

2 Spray the broiler rack with nonstick spray and preheat the broiler.

3 Place the steak on the broiler rack and broil 4 inches from the heat until an instant-read thermometer inserted into the side of the steak registers 145°F for medium-rare, about 8 minutes on each side. Transfer the steak to a cutting board and let stand 5 minutes. Cut the steak into 6 portions.

PER SERVING (1 piece steak): 244 Cal, 9 g Fat, 4 g Sat Fat, 0 g Trans Fat, 59 mg Chol, 520 mg Sod, 7 g Carb, 0 g Fib, 32 g Prot, 14 mg Calc. *POINTS* value: *6.*

Filling Extra

Before broiling the steak, grill 3 assorted color bell peppers and a couple of whole spring onions—tops still attached—or regular onions, halved or quartered, until tender.

MAPLE AND
CHILI–BROILED
T-BONE STEAK

CURRIED BEEF KEBABS WITH
BROWN BASMATI RICE

Curried Beef Kebabs with Brown Basmati Rice

PREP 10 MIN | **COOK/BROIL** 10 MIN | **SERVES** 4

- **1 cup brown basmati rice**
- **1¼ pounds boneless sirloin steak, trimmed and cut into 1-inch chunks**
- **1 red onion, quartered and separated into slices**
- **1 yellow squash, sliced**
- **4 baby patty pan squash, halved**
- **2 teaspoons canola oil**
- **2½ teaspoons curry powder**
- **¾ teaspoon salt**
- **¼ cup lightly packed fresh cilantro leaves**

1 Prepare the rice according to the package directions, omitting the salt if desired.

2 Spray the broiler rack with nonstick spray and preheat the broiler.

3 Toss together all the remaining ingredients except the cilantro in a large bowl.

4 Thread the beef, onion, and squash alternately on 8 (12-inch) metal skewers. Place the skewers on the prepared broiler rack and broil 5 inches from the heat, turning occasionally, until an instant-read thermometer inserted into a chunk of beef registers 145°F for medium-rare, about 10 minutes. Serve with the rice and sprinkle with the cilantro.

PER SERVING (2 skewers and ¾ cup rice): 435 Cal, 8 g Fat, 2 g Sat Fat, 0 g Trans Fat, 92 mg Chol, 1035 mg Sod, 46 g Carb, 2 g Fib, 42 g Prot, 39 mg Calc. *POINTS* value: *9.*

In the Kitchen

Look for brown basmati rice at your supermarket. Although it takes about 20 minutes longer to cook than white basmati rice, its enticing nutty flavor, extra fiber, and appealing texture make it worth the extra time. This recipe works with the Simply Filling technique.

Gingered Beef and Broccoli

PREP 10 MIN | **COOK** 10 MIN | **SERVES** 2

- **2 teaspoons Asian (dark) sesame oil**
- **10 ounces sirloin steak, trimmed and cut into strips**
- **1 tablespoon minced peeled fresh ginger**
- **2 garlic cloves, minced**
- **1 (10-ounce) package frozen broccoli florets, thawed**
- **4 scallions, cut into 1-inch lengths**
- **1 tablespoon reduced-sodium soy sauce**
- **½ teaspoon hot chili paste (optional)**

1 Heat a large deep nonstick skillet or wok over high heat until a drop of water sizzles in the pan. Add the oil and swirl to coat the skillet. Add the steak and stir-fry until lightly browned, about 2 minutes. Transfer to a plate.

2 Add the ginger and garlic to the skillet and stir-fry until fragrant, about 30 seconds. Add the broccoli and scallions and stir-fry until just softened, about 2 minutes longer.

3 Return the steak to the skillet along with the soy sauce and chili paste, if using. Stir-fry until the beef is just cooked through, about 2 minutes longer.

PER SERVING **(1½ cups): 262 Cal, 11 g Fat, 3 g Sat Fat, 1 g Trans Fat, 80 mg Chol, 400 mg Sod, 10 g Carb, 5 g Fib, 32 g Prot, 113 mg Calc.** *POINTS* value: *5*.

Filling Extra

Think beyond the usual rice accompaniment and consider serving this savory stir-fry with soba noodles (1 cup of cooked soba noodles per serving will increase the *POINTS* value by ***2***).

Caesar-Style Steak Salad

PREP 5 MIN | **COOK** 10 MIN | **SERVES** 2

- **6 ounces top round or boneless sirloin steak, trimmed**
- **¼ teaspoon black pepper**
- **⅛ teaspoon salt**
- **1 head romaine lettuce, chopped (about 8 cups)**
- **½ red onion, thinly sliced**
- **¼ cup fat-free Caesar dressing**
- **¼ cup grated Parmesan cheese**

1 Heat a nonstick ridged grill pan or cast-iron skillet over high heat. Sprinkle the steak with the pepper and salt. Place the steak on the pan and cook until an instant-read thermometer inserted into the side of the steak registers 145°F for medium-rare, about 4 minutes on each side. Transfer to a cutting board and let stand 5 minutes.

2 Toss together the remaining ingredients in a large bowl. Divide the salad evenly between 2 plates. Cut the steak into 10 slices and divide evenly between the salads.

PER SERVING (3 cups salad and 5 slices steak): 213 Cal, 6 g Fat, 3 g Sat Fat, 1 g Trans Fat, 57 mg Chol, 866 mg Sod, 11 g Carb, 4 g Fib, 27 g Prot, 246 mg Calc. *POINTS* value: *4.*

In the Kitchen

We suggest round or sirloin for this salad because it's commonly available and usually a good buy, but other lean choices include flank steak and filet mignon.

Roasted Leg of Lamb

PREP 10 MIN | **ROAST** 1 HR | **SERVES** 8

- **3 garlic cloves, minced**
- **1 tablespoon paprika**
- **2 teaspoons poultry seasoning**
- **1½ teaspoons salt**
- **½ teaspoon black pepper**
- **1 (2¼-pound) boneless leg of lamb, trimmed**
- **4 onions, sliced**
- **¾ cup dry white wine or dry vermouth**

1 Preheat the oven to 400°F. Lightly spray a roasting pan with nonstick spray.

2 Stir together the garlic, paprika, poultry seasoning, salt, and pepper in a small bowl. Add enough water to form a thick paste and rub all over the lamb.

3 Place the lamb in the prepared roasting pan and top with the onions. Pour the wine into the pan. Roast until an instant-read thermometer inserted into the center of the lamb registers 145°F for medium-rare, about 1 hour.

4 Transfer the lamb to a cutting board and let stand 10 minutes. Cut into 24 slices and serve with the onions.

PER SERVING (3 slices lamb and about ½ cup onion): 240 Cal, 9 g Fat, 3 g Sat Fat, 0 g Trans Fat, 88 mg Chol, 530 mg Sod, 10 g Carb, 2 g Fib, 28 g Prot, 32 mg Calc. *POINTS* value: *5.*

Filling Extra

For the perfect side to the roast, arrange in overlapping rows in a shallow baking dish sprayed with olive oil nonstick spray, 4 zucchini, sliced, and 8 small tomatoes, sliced. Sprinkle with fresh or dried thyme, salt, and pepper; spray lightly with nonstick spray. Bake alongside the lamb.

Super-Fast Barbecued Chicken

PREP 5 MIN | **COOK** 10 MIN | **SERVES** 4

- **3 tablespoons ketchup**
- **1 tablespoon hoisin sauce**
- **1 tablespoon apple-cider vinegar**
- **2 teaspoons molasses**
- **2 teaspoons reduced-sodium soy sauce**
- **4 (1/4-pound) cooked skinless boneless chicken breasts**

1 Stir together all the ingredients except the chicken in a small bowl.

2 Spray a nonstick ridged grill pan with nonstick spray and set over medium heat. Brush the sauce on both sides of the chicken. Place the chicken on the pan and cook just until nicely glazed and heated through, about 5 minutes on each side.

PER SERVING (1 chicken breast): 228 Cal, 5 g Fat, 1 g Sat Fat, 0 g Trans Fat, 97 mg Chol, 745 mg Sod, 7 g Carb, 0 g Fib, 36 g Prot, 28 mg Calc. *POINTS* value: *5.*

In the Kitchen

Poached, broiled, baked, and grilled skinless boneless chicken breasts can be found in the prepared food section of many large supermarkets and in specialty food stores.

Quick Chicken Satay with Asparagus

PREP 10 MIN | **ROAST** 15 MIN | **SERVES** 2

- **2** **(5-ounce) skinless boneless chicken breasts, each cut into 6 long strips**
- **5** **teaspoons reduced-sodium teriyaki sauce**
- **16** **asparagus spears, trimmed**
- **2** **teaspoons reduced-sodium soy sauce**
- **2** **teaspoons canola oil**

1 Preheat the oven to 375°F. Line a baking sheet with foil and spray with nonstick spray. Soak 6 (12-inch) wooden skewers in water 30 minutes.

2 Toss together the chicken and teriyaki sauce in a medium bowl.

3 Thread 2 pieces of chicken on each skewer and arrange on the prepared baking sheet. Place the asparagus next to the chicken in one layer. Brush the asparagus with the soy sauce and oil. Roast until the chicken is cooked through and the asparagus is tender, about 15 minutes.

PER SERVING **(3 skewers and 8 asparagus spears): 256 Cal, 9 g Fat, 2 g Sat Fat, 0 g Trans Fat, 86 mg Chol, 700 mg Sod, 7 g Carb, 3 g Fib, 35 g Prot, 49 mg Calc.** *POINTS* value: *5.*

Filling Extra

Serve the satay over a bed of hot brown basmati rice or wild rice, or a combination of rices (½ cup cooked brown basmati rice per serving will increase the *POINTS* value by ***2***).

This recipe works with the Simply Filling technique.

QUICK CHICKEN SATAY
WITH ASPARAGUS

Easy Chicken Cutlets Parmesan

PREP 5 MIN | **COOK/MICROWAVE** 10 MIN | **SERVES** 2

- **4** **(3-ounce) chicken cutlets**
- **½** **cup fat-free marinara sauce**
- **1** **cup shredded fat-free mozzarella cheese**
- **2** **tablespoons grated Parmesan cheese**
- **2** **tablespoons chopped fresh basil**

1 Spray a large nonstick skillet with nonstick spray and set over medium-high heat. Add the chicken and cook until browned and cooked through, about 2 minutes on each side.

2 Place the chicken in a small baking dish in one layer and layer evenly with the marinara sauce, mozzarella, and Parmesan. Microwave on High until the cheese is melted, about 2 minutes. Sprinkle with the basil.

PER SERVING (2 cutlets): 363 Cal, 8 g Fat, 3 g Sat Fat, 0 g Trans Fat, 117 mg Chol, 1134 mg Sod, 13 g Carb, 1 g Fib, 57 g Prot, 624 mg Calc. *POINTS* value: *8.*

Filling Extra

Go Italian with a tasty side of sautéed zucchini. Sprinkle 2 zucchini, thinly sliced, with red pepper flakes and salt. Cook in a nonstick skillet sprayed with olive oil nonstick spray until lightly browned and tender, about 6 minutes.

Chicken Picadillo

PREP 10 MIN | **COOK** 20 MIN | **SERVES** 4

- **2 teaspoons olive oil**
- **1 onion, chopped**
- **2 garlic cloves, minced**
- **1 pound ground skinless chicken breast**
- **1 (14½-ounce) can diced tomatoes**
- **¼ cup dark raisins**
- **¼ cup pimiento-stuffed olives, coarsely chopped**
- **1 teaspoon ground cumin**
- **½ teaspoon salt**
- **¼ teaspoon black pepper**
- **¼ cup slivered almonds**

1 Heat the oil in a large skillet over medium heat. Add the onion and garlic and cook, stirring, until softened, about 5 minutes.

2 Add the chicken to the skillet. Cook, breaking up the chicken with a wooden spoon, until browned, about 8 minutes.

3 Stir in all the remaining ingredients except the almonds and bring to a boil over medium-high heat. Reduce the heat and simmer until slightly thickened, about 5 minutes. Stir in the almonds.

PER SERVING (generous 1 cup): 278 Cal, 12 g Fat, 2 g Sat Fat, 0 g Trans Fat, 68 mg Chol, 652 mg Sod, 17 g Carb, 3 g Fib, 28 g Prot, 84 mg Calc. *POINTS* value: *6.*

Grilled Chicken and Jack Cheese Sandwiches

PREP 5 MIN | **COOK** 10 MIN | **SERVES** 2

- **4 slices reduced-calorie whole-wheat bread**
- **2 teaspoons Dijon mustard**
- **6 ounces thinly sliced reduced-sodium deli chicken breast**
- **1 small tomato, sliced**
- **2 (¾-ounce) slices reduced-fat pepper Jack cheese**

1 Spread 2 slices of the bread with the mustard. Layer evenly with the chicken, tomato, and pepper Jack. Top with the remaining 2 slices of bread. Spray the top slices of bread with olive oil nonstick spray.

2 Heat a large nonstick skillet over medium heat. Place the sandwiches in the skillet, sprayed side down, and cook until nicely browned, about 3 minutes. Spray the tops of the sandwiches with nonstick spray. Turn and cook until the bread is browned and the cheese begins to melt, about 3 minutes longer.

PER SERVING (1 sandwich): 342 Cal, 11 g Fat, 4 g Sat Fat, 0 g Trans Fat, 87 mg Chol, 648 mg Sod, 21 g Carb, 4 g Fib, 38 g Prot, 220 mg Calc. *POINTS* value: *7.*

Filling Extra

Make these sandwiches even more flavorful—and satisfying—by adding 1 sliced scallion and ½ small red bell pepper, chopped, to the sandwich filling.

Mexicali Chicken Salad

PREP 15 MIN | **COOK** NONE | **SERVES** 4

- **¾ cup salsa**
- **¼ cup fat-free ranch dressing**
- **1 head romaine lettuce, chopped (about 8 cups)**
- **1 large tomato, diced**
- **1 small jicama, peeled and shredded**
- **1 cup shredded reduced-fat Monterey Jack or pepper Jack cheese**
- **1 cup canned black beans, rinsed and drained**
- **2 cups diced cooked chicken breast**
- **12 baked tortilla chips, broken up**

1 Stir together the salsa and ranch dressing in a serving bowl. Add the lettuce, tomato, jicama, Monterey Jack, and beans; toss to coat.

2 Divide the salad evenly among 4 plates. Top the salads evenly with the chicken and sprinkle with the tortilla chips.

PER SERVING (3 cups salad, ½ cup chicken, and 3 tortilla chips): 384 Cal, 10 g Fat, 5 g Sat Fat, 0 g Trans Fat, 80 mg Chol, 980 mg Sod, 38 g Carb, 12 g Fib, 37 g Prot, 297 mg Calc. *POINTS* value: *8.*

Mediterranean Turkey Burgers

PREP 10 MIN | **COOK** 10 MIN | **SERVES** 4

- **1 pound ground skinless turkey breast**
- **¾ teaspoon dried oregano**
- **¼ teaspoon black pepper**
- **½ cup crumbled reduced-fat feta cheese**
- **2 teaspoons olive oil**
- **2 large whole-wheat pitas, halved**
- **1 (5-ounce) jar roasted red pepper, drained**
- **2 cups mixed baby salad greens**

1 Mix together the turkey, oregano, and black pepper in a large bowl. With damp hands, shape the mixture into 8 thin patties.

2 Place 2 tablespoons of the feta in the middle of each of 4 patties. Top with the remaining patties and pinch the edges to enclose the cheese and to seal the patties.

3 Heat the oil in a large skillet over medium heat. Add the burgers and cook until an instant-read thermometer inserted into the side of a burger (without touching the cheese) registers 160°F for well done, about 5 minutes on each side.

4 Place each burger in a pita half. Top evenly with the roasted red pepper and salad greens.

PER SERVING (1 stuffed pita): 317 Cal, 8 g Fat, 4 g Sat Fat, 0 g Trans Fat, 91 mg Chol, 717 mg Sod, 25 g Carb, 3 g Fib, 34 g Prot, 139 mg Calc. *POINTS* value: *6.*

Warm Lentil Salad with Baked Salmon

PREP 15 MIN | **COOK/BAKE** 15 MIN | **SERVES** 4

- **4 cups water**
- **1 cup green (French) lentils, picked over and rinsed**
- **1 (1-pound) piece center-cut salmon fillet, skinned**
- **½ teaspoon salt**
- **¼ teaspoon black pepper**
- **½ red bell pepper, peeled and chopped**
- **¼ cup reduced-sodium chicken broth**
- **2 teaspoons olive oil**
- **1¼ teaspoons white-wine vinegar**
- **½ teaspoon salt**
- **2 cups torn frisée lettuce**
- **½ small red onion, finely chopped**

1 Preheat the oven to 300°F. Line a baking sheet with foil.

2 Bring the water to a boil in a medium saucepan. Add the lentils and cook until just tender, about 15 minutes; drain.

3 Meanwhile, put the salmon, skinned side down, on the prepared baking sheet. Sprinkle with the salt and black pepper. Bake until just opaque in the center, about 15 minutes.

4 Puree the bell pepper, broth, oil, vinegar, and salt in a blender. Transfer the mixture to a large bowl. Add the lentils, lettuce, and onion and toss to combine.

5 Cut the salmon into 4 portions and put 1 piece of salmon on each of 4 plates. Spoon the lentil salad alongside.

PER SERVING (1 piece salmon and 1¼ cups salad): 347 Cal, 9 g Fat, 2 g Sat Fat, 0 Trans Fat, 75 mg Chol, 709 mg Sod, 29 g Carb, 9 g Fib, 37 g Prot, 65 mg Calc. *POINTS* value: *7.*

In the Kitchen

A vegetable peeler makes quick work of removing the bell pepper peel. Don't worry if small bits of the peel remain. It will not be noticeable once the bell pepper is pureed. This recipe works with the Simply Filling technique.

Grilled Salmon with Quick Tapenade

PREP 10 MIN | **COOK** 10 MIN | **SERVES** 4

- **4 (¼-pound) skinless salmon fillets**
- **¼ teaspoon salt**
- **⅛ teaspoon black pepper**
- **¼ cup pitted kalamata olives**
- **¼ cup coarsely chopped rehydrated sun-dried tomatoes (not packed in oil)**
- **3 tablespoons coarsely chopped fresh basil or parsley**
- **2 tablespoons pine nuts**

1 Spray a nonstick ridged grill pan with nonstick spray and set over medium-high heat. Sprinkle the salmon with the salt and pepper. Place the salmon on the pan and cook until just opaque in the center, about 4 minutes on each side.

2 Meanwhile, to make the tapenade, put the remaining ingredients in a mini–food processor and process until chopped.

3 Top the salmon evenly with the tapenade.

PER SERVING (1 salmon fillet and 2½ tablespoons tapenade): 201 Cal, 9 g Fat, 1 g Sat Fat, 0 g Trans Fat, 65 mg Chol, 437 mg Sod, 3 g Carb, 1 g Fib, 26 g Prot, 28 mg Calc. *POINTS* value: *5.*

Filling Extra

Serve the salmon with some crisp watercress sprigs.

GRILLED SALMON WITH QUICK TAPENADE

CALIFORNIA
FISH TACOS

California Fish Tacos

PREP 10 MIN | **BROIL** 10 MIN | **SERVES** 4

- **2 (6-ounce) skinless halibut fillets**
- **½ teaspoon salt**
- **¼ teaspoon ground cumin**
- **8 small taco shells**
- **1 cup thinly sliced romaine lettuce**
- **1 avocado, halved, pitted, peeled, and diced**
- **¼ cup chopped fresh cilantro**
- **1 lime, cut into 8 wedges**
- **½ cup fat-free salsa**

1 Spray the broiler rack with nonstick spray and preheat the broiler.

2 Sprinkle the halibut with the salt and cumin. Place the fillets on the broiler rack and broil 5 inches from the heat until the fish is just opaque throughout, about 3 minutes on each side. Transfer the fish to a plate and use a fork to flake the fish.

3 Divide the fish evenly among the taco shells. Top evenly with the lettuce, avocado, and cilantro. Serve with the lime wedges and salsa.

PER SERVING (2 tacos and 2 tablespoons salsa): 295 Cal, 12 g Fat, 2 g Sat Fat, 0 g Trans Fat, 60 mg Chol, 685 mg Sod, 23 g Carb, 5 g Fib, 25 g Prot, 66 mg Calc. *POINTS* value: *6*.

In the Kitchen

Halibut has a firm texture, so it breaks into big, juicy flakes that are perfect in tacos. Other good choices that will flake—not turn to mush—include mahimahi, cod, and salmon.

Creole-Style Cod Fillets

PREP 10 MIN | **COOK** 15 MIN | **SERVES** 4

- **2 cups spicy vegetable or tomato juice**
- **2 green bell peppers, thinly sliced**
- **1 onion, thinly sliced**
- **2 celery stalks, thinly sliced**
- **4 (6-ounce) cod fillets**
- **2 tablespoons chopped fresh parsley**
- **2 cups hot cooked brown rice**

1 Combine the vegetable juice, bell peppers, onion, and celery in a large nonstick skillet; bring to a boil over medium-high heat. Reduce the heat and simmer until the vegetables are just softened, about 4 minutes.

2 Nestle the cod into the vegetables. Reduce the heat and simmer, covered, until the fish is just opaque throughout, about 8 minutes. Sprinkle with the parsley and serve with the rice.

PER SERVING (1 cod fillet, 1 cup vegetables with sauce, and ½ cup rice): 313 Cal, 3 g Fat, 1 g Sat Fat, 0 g Trans Fat, 90 mg Chol, 761 mg Sod, 34 g Carb, 6 g Fib, 36 g Prot, 70 mg Calc. *POINTS* value: *6.*

Filling Extra

For an easy and earthy addition to the Creole sauce, add an 8-ounce package of sliced white or cremini mushrooms along with the bell peppers.

Linguine with Fontina and Artichokes

PREP 10 MIN | **COOK** 25 MIN | **SERVES** 4

- **6 ounces whole-wheat linguine**
- **4 plum tomatoes, chopped**
- **2 garlic cloves, minced**
- **1 (9-ounce) package frozen quartered artichoke hearts, thawed**
- **⅛ teaspoon black pepper**
- **4 ounces fontina cheese, diced**
- **½ cup thinly sliced fresh basil**

1 Cook the linguine according to the package directions, omitting the salt if desired. Drain the linguine, reserving ½ cup of the cooking water.

2 Add the tomatoes and garlic to the pasta pot. Cook over medium heat, stirring, until the tomatoes begin to soften, about 2 minutes.

3 Return the pasta to the pot along with the artichokes and pepper. Cook, stirring, until heated through, about 4 minutes. (If the pasta seems dry, stir in some of the reserved cooking water

4 Transfer the pasta mixture to a serving bowl. Add the fontina and basil; toss to combine.

PER SERVING (1½ cups): 310 Cal, 10 g Fat, 6 g Sat Fat, 0 g Trans Fat, 33 mg Chol, 452 mg Sod, 44 g Carb, 8 g Fib, 17 g Prot, 221 mg Calc. *POINTS* value: *6.*

Filling Extra

About 2 minutes before the pasta has finished cooking, add 2 cups small broccoli florets to the pot.

Shrimp and Spaghetti Arrabbiata

PREP 15 MIN | **COOK** 15 MIN | **SERVES** 4

- **8 ounces whole-wheat spaghetti**
- **4 teaspoons olive oil**
- **1 pound large shrimp, peeled and deveined, tails left on if desired**
- **¾ teaspoon salt**
- **3 garlic cloves, minced**
- **1 (15-ounce) can crushed tomatoes**
- **3 tablespoons tomato paste**
- **½ teaspoon dried oregano**
- **¼ teaspoon red pepper flakes**
- **6 large basil leaves, thinly sliced**

1 Cook the spaghetti according to the package directions, omitting the salt if desired. Drain and keep warm.

2 Meanwhile, heat 2 teaspoons of the oil in a large nonstick skillet over medium-high heat. Sprinkle the shrimp with ½ teaspoon of the salt. Add the shrimp to the skillet, in two batches, and cook until just opaque in the center, about 2 minutes on each side.

3 Heat the remaining 2 teaspoons oil in the skillet over medium heat. Add the garlic and cook, stirring, until fragrant, about 30 seconds. Stir in the tomatoes, tomato paste, oregano, and red pepper flakes; cook until slightly thickened, about 5 minutes. Add the shrimp, basil, and the remaining ¼ teaspoon salt; cook, stirring occasionally, just until the shrimp are heated through, about 1 minute longer.

4 Divide the pasta evenly among 4 plates and top evenly with the shrimp and sauce.

PER SERVING (1 cup pasta and about ½ cup shrimp with sauce): 367 Cal, 7 g Fat, 1 g Sat Fat, 0 g Trans Fat, 168 mg Chol, 782 mg Sod, 52 g Carb, 10 g Fib, 29 g Prot, 102 mg Calc. *POINTS* value: *7.*

Tip

This recipe works with the Simply Filling technique.

SHRIMP AND SPAGHETTI ARRABBIATA

LENTIL AND SAUSAGE SOUP

Lentil and Sausage Soup

PREP 15 MIN | **COOK** 40 MIN | **SERVES** 4

- **2 teaspoons olive oil**
- **2 carrots, thinly sliced**
- **1 onion, diced**
- **2 garlic cloves, minced**
- **¼ pound turkey kielbasa, thinly sliced**
- **1¼ cups brown lentils, picked over and rinsed**
- **5 cups water**
- **1 (14½-ounce) can diced tomatoes**
- **½ teaspoon salt**
- **¼ teaspoon black pepper**

1 Heat the oil in a large saucepan over medium heat. Add the carrots, onion, and garlic; cook, stirring frequently, until softened, about 5 minutes.

2 Add the kielbasa, lentils, and water; bring to a boil. Reduce the heat and simmer until the lentils are tender, about 30 minutes.

3 Stir in the tomatoes, salt, and pepper. Simmer until heated through, about 5 minutes longer.

PER SERVING (1¾ cups): 296 Cal, 6 g Fat, 1 g Sat Fat, 0 g Trans Fat, 15 mg Chol, 760 mg Sod, 44 g Carb, 12 g Fib, 21 g Prot, 95 mg Calc. *POINTS* value: *6.*

SLICED STEAK WITH CRISPY POLENTA

Sliced Steak with Crispy Polenta

PREP 15 MIN | **COOK/BROIL** 15 MIN | **SERVES** 4

- **1 (1-pound) flank steak, trimmed**
- **½ teaspoon ancho or regular chili powder**
- **½ teaspoon salt**
- **1 (16-ounce) tube fat-free polenta, cut into 12 slices**
- **1½ cups fresh or thawed frozen corn kernels**
- **1 red bell pepper, chopped**
- **½ red onion, chopped**
- **1 jalapeño pepper, seeded and minced**
- **2 tablespoons chopped fresh cilantro**

1 Spray a nonstick ridged grill pan with nonstick spray and set over medium-high heat. Sprinkle the steak with the chili powder and salt. Place the steak on the pan and cook until an instant-read thermometer inserted into the side of the steak registers 145°F for medium-rare, about 5 minutes on each side. Transfer the steak to a cutting board and let stand 5 minutes. Cut on a diagonal into 16 slices.

2 Meanwhile, spray the broiler rack with nonstick spray and preheat the broiler. Arrange the slices of polenta on the rack and broil 5 inches from the heat until crispy and heated through, about 2 minutes on each side.

3 Spray a medium nonstick skillet with nonstick spray and set over medium heat. Add the corn, bell pepper, onion, and jalapeño pepper; cook, stirring, until softened, about 5 minutes. Remove the skillet from the heat and stir in the cilantro.

4 Place 3 slices of polenta on each of 4 plates and top evenly with the steak. Spoon the corn mixture on top.

PER SERVING (4 slices steak, 3 slices polenta, and ¾ cup corn mixture): 312 Cal, 5 g Fat, 2 g Sat Fat, 1 g Trans Fat, 83 mg Chol, 345 mg Sod, 29 g Carb, 3 g Fib, 37 g Prot, 16 mg Calc. *POINTS* value: *6*.

Tip

This recipe works with the Simply Filling technique.

Stir-Fried Beef and Asparagus

PREP 10 MIN | **COOK** 15 MIN | **SERVES** 4

- **1** **cup quick-cooking brown rice**
- **2** **teaspoons canola oil**
- **1** **pound top round steak, trimmed and cut into thin strips**
- **4** **garlic cloves, thinly sliced**
- **1** **tablespoon minced peeled fresh ginger**
- **1** **pound asparagus spears, trimmed and cut into 2-inch pieces**
- **1** **red bell pepper, thinly sliced**
- **4** **scallions, thinly sliced**
- **1** **(5-ounce) can sliced water chestnuts, drained**
- **¾** **cup chicken broth**
- **1** **tablespoon reduced-sodium soy sauce**

1 Cook the rice according to the package directions, omitting the salt if desired.

2 Meanwhile, heat a large deep nonstick skillet or wok over high heat until a drop of water sizzles in the pan. Add the oil and swirl to coat the skillet. Add the beef and stir-fry until browned and cooked through, about 4 minutes. With a slotted spoon, transfer the beef to a plate.

3 Add the garlic and ginger to the skillet and stir-fry until fragrant, about 30 seconds. Add the asparagus and bell pepper and stir-fry until crisp-tender, about 2 minutes longer. Return the beef to the skillet and add the remaining ingredients. Stir-fry until the liquid is reduced, about 3 minutes longer. Serve with the rice.

PER SERVING (1⅓ cups beef mixture and ½ cup rice): 354 Cal, 8 g Fat, 2 g Sat Fat, 0 g Trans Fat, 84 mg Chol, 810 mg Sod, 30 g Carb, 6 g Fib, 39 g Prot, 53 mg Calc. *POINTS* value: *7.*

Filling Extra

Stir in any of the following vegetables along with the asparagus: a handful of snow peas, 1 sliced onion, 2 thinly sliced carrots, or 6 sliced shiitake mushroom caps. This recipe works with the Simply Filling technique.

STIR-FRIED
BEEF AND
ASPARAGUS

Kasha and Mixed Vegetable Pilaf

PREP 10 MIN | **COOK** 20 MIN | **SERVES** 4

- **2 cups reduced-sodium vegetable broth**
- **4 teaspoons olive oil**
- **1 red onion, chopped**
- **1 zucchini, cut into small dice**
- **1 green bell pepper, cut into small dice**
- **1 cup canned cannellini (white kidney beans), rinsed and drained**
- **2 garlic cloves, minced**
- **¾ teaspoon salt**
- **1 cup coarse kasha**
- **1 large egg, lightly beaten**
- **¼ teaspoon black pepper**

1 Bring the broth to a boil in a small saucepan.

2 Meanwhile, heat 2 teaspoons of the oil in a large nonstick skillet over medium-high heat. Add the onion, zucchini, and bell pepper; cook, stirring occasionally, until softened, about 5 minutes. Add the beans, garlic, and ¼ teaspoon of the salt: cook, stirring frequently, 1 minute. Transfer the vegetable mixture to a bowl; keep warm.

3 Stir together the kasha and egg in a medium bowl until the grains are coated. Heat the remaining 2 teaspoons oil in the same skillet over medium-high heat. Add the kasha mixture and cook, stirring constantly with a wooden spoon, until all the grains separate, about 4 minutes. Stir in the broth, the remaining ½ teaspoon salt, and the black pepper. Reduce the heat and simmer, covered, until the broth is absorbed, about 10 minutes. Add the vegetable mixture and cook, stirring occasionally, until heated through, about 1 minute longer.

PER SERVING (1½ cups): 293 Cal, 8 g Fat, 1 g Sat Fat, 0 g Trans Fat, 53 mg Chol, 884 mg Sod, 47 g Carb, 9 g Fib, 12 g Prot, 52 mg Calc. *POINTS* value: *6.*

Tip

This recipe works with the Simply Filling technique.

Easy Chicken Florentine with Spaghetti

PREP 10 MIN | **COOK/BAKE** 35 MIN | **SERVES** 4

- **2 teaspoons olive oil**
- **1 small onion, chopped**
- **2 (10-ounce) packages frozen leaf spinach, thawed**
- **½ teaspoon salt**
- **¼ teaspoon black pepper**
- **4 (5-ounce) skinless boneless chicken breasts**
- **1 cup shredded fat-free mozzarella cheese**
- **2 tablespoons grated Parmesan cheese**
- **4 ounces whole-wheat spaghetti**
- **2 slices bacon, crisp cooked and crumbled**
- **½ cup fat-free marinara sauce, heated**

1 Preheat the oven to 350°F. Spray an 8-inch square baking dish with nonstick spray.

2 Heat 1 teaspoon of the oil in a large nonstick skillet over medium-high heat. Add the onion and cook, stirring frequently, until softened, about 5 minutes. Add the spinach, ¼ teaspoon of the salt, and the pepper to the skillet. Cook until most of the liquid is evaporated, about 5 minutes longer. Spoon the spinach mixture evenly into the prepared baking dish.

3 Wipe out the skillet. Add the remaining 1 teaspoon oil to the skillet and set over high heat. Sprinkle the chicken with the remaining ¼ teaspoon salt. Place the chicken in the skillet and cook just until browned, about 2 minutes on each side.

4 Arrange the chicken over the spinach mixture in one layer; sprinkle evenly with the mozzarella and Parmesan. Bake until the cheeses are melted and the chicken is cooked through, about 20 minutes. Sprinkle with the bacon.

5 Meanwhile, cook the spaghetti according to the package directions, omitting the salt if desired. Drain. Toss together the spaghetti and marinara sauce. Serve with the chicken.

PER SERVING (¼ of casserole and ½ cup pasta): 432 Cal, 11 g Fat, 3 g Sat Fat, 0 g Trans Fat, 97 mg Chol, 1157 mg Sod, 35 g Carb, 7 g Fib, 51 g Prot, 473 mg Calc. *POINTS* value: *9.*

GRILLED CHICKEN WITH RASPBERRY AND GOAT CHEESE SALAD

Grilled Chicken with Raspberry and Goat Cheese Salad

PREP 5 MIN | **COOK** 10 MIN | **SERVES** 4

- **4 (¼-pound) chicken cutlets**
- **¾ teaspoon salt**
- **1 (7-ounce) bag mixed baby salad greens**
- **2 tablespoons raspberry or red-wine vinegar**
- **2 teaspoons olive oil**
- **¼ teaspoon black pepper**
- **½ cup crumbled soft (mild) goat cheese**
- **2 (6-ounce) containers raspberries**
- **3 scallions, thinly sliced**

1 Spray a nonstick ridged grill pan with nonstick spray and set over medium-high heat. Sprinkle the chicken with ½ teaspoon of the salt. Place the chicken on the pan and cook until cooked through, about 3 minutes on each side.

2 Meanwhile, toss together the salad greens, vinegar, oil, the remaining ¼ teaspoon salt, and the pepper until coated.

3 Add the goat cheese, raspberries, and scallions to the salad and gently toss to combine. Divide the salad evenly among 4 plates. Halve the cutlets and place 2 pieces on top of each salad.

PER SERVING (1 chicken cutlet and 2 cups salad): 252 Cal, 10 g Fat, 4 g Sat Fat, 0 g Trans Fat, 76 mg Chol, 586 mg Sod, 10 g Carb, 5 g Fib, 30 g Prot, 85 mg Calc. *POINTS* value: *5.*

Grilled Ginger Chicken with Peach Salsa

PREP 15 MIN | **COOK** 10 MIN | **SERVES** 4

- **4 (¼-pound) chicken cutlets**
- **2 teaspoons minced peeled fresh ginger**
- **1 garlic clove, minced**
- **2 teaspoons canola oil**
- **½ teaspoon salt**
- **3 peaches, diced**
- **1 tomato, diced**
- **½ small red onion, chopped**
- **1 jalapeño pepper, seeded and minced**
- **¼ cup chopped fresh cilantro**
- **2 teaspoons lime juice**

1 Combine the chicken, ginger, garlic, oil, and ¼ teaspoon of the salt in a large zip-close plastic bag. Squeeze out the air and seal the bag; turn to coat the chicken. Refrigerate, turning the bag occasionally, at least 30 minutes or up to overnight.

2 Meanwhile, to make the salsa, toss together the peaches, tomato, onion, jalapeño pepper, cilantro, lime juice, and the remaining ¼ teaspoon salt in a serving bowl.

3 Spray a nonstick ridged grill pan with nonstick spray and set over medium-high heat. Remove the chicken from the marinade and place in the pan; discard the marinade. Cook the chicken until cooked through, about 3 minutes on each side. Serve with the peach salsa.

PER SERVING (1 chicken cutlet and about 1 cup salsa): 218 Cal, 6 g Fat, 1 g Sat Fat, 0 g Trans Fat, 68 mg Chol, 360 mg Sod, 14 g Carb, 2 g Fib, 26 g Prot, 27 mg Calc. ***POINTS* value: *4.***

Tip

This recipe works with the Simply Filling technique.

Chicken Puttanesca with Pasta

PREP 10 MIN | **COOK** 20 MIN | **SERVES** 4

- **4 ounces whole-wheat penne**
- **⅔ cup dried seasoned bread crumbs**
- **1 large egg**
- **2 teaspoons olive oil**
- **4 (¼-pound) chicken cutlets**
- **6 plum tomatoes, chopped**
- **3 anchovy fillets, minced**
- **2 garlic cloves, minced**
- **1½ tablespoons drained capers**
- **1 teaspoon balsamic vinegar**
- **⅛ teaspoon red pepper flakes**

1 Cook the penne according to the package directions, omitting the salt if desired. Drain and keep warm.

2 Place the bread crumbs on a sheet of wax paper. Beat the egg lightly in a large shallow bowl or pie plate. Dip the chicken cutlets into the egg, then coat on both sides with the bread crumbs, pressing lightly so they adhere.

3 Heat the oil in a large nonstick skillet over medium heat. Add the chicken to the skillet and cook until browned and cooked through, about 3 minutes on each side. Transfer to a platter and keep warm.

4 Add the tomatoes, anchovies, garlic, capers, vinegar, and red pepper flakes to the skillet. Cook, stirring occasionally, until the tomatoes are softened, about 5 minutes. Spoon the sauce over the chicken and serve with the pasta.

PER SERVING **(1 chicken cutlet, ½ cup sauce, and ½ cup pasta): 373 Cal, 9 g Fat, 2 g Sat Fat, 0 g Trans Fat, 124 mg Chol, 520 mg Sod, 38 g Carb, 4 g Fib, 35 g Prot, 93 mg Calc.** ***POINTS*** **value:** ***7.***

Teriyaki Chicken and Snow Pea Stir-Fry

PREP 15 MIN | **COOK** 15 MIN | **SERVES** 4

- **2 teaspoons Asian (dark) sesame oil**
- **1 pound skinless boneless chicken breasts, cut into thin strips**
- **2 garlic cloves, minced**
- **1 (½-inch) piece fresh ginger, peeled and minced**
- **1 red bell pepper, thinly sliced**
- **4 scallions, thinly sliced**
- **1 (5-ounce) can sliced water chestnuts, drained**
- **6 ounces snow peas, trimmed**
- **¼ cup reduced-sodium chicken broth**
- **2 tablespoons teriyaki sauce**
- **Pinch red pepper flakes**
- **4 cups hot cooked brown rice**

1 Heat a large deep nonstick skillet or wok over medium-high heat until a drop of water sizzles in the pan. Add the oil and swirl to coat the skillet. Add the chicken to the skillet and stir-fry until browned and cooked through, about 5 minutes. With a slotted spoon, transfer the chicken to a plate.

2 Add the garlic and ginger to the skillet and stir-fry until fragrant, about 30 seconds. Add the bell pepper, scallions, and water chestnuts; stir-fry 2 minutes. Add the snow peas and stir-fry until bright green. Add the broth, teriyaki sauce, and red pepper flakes; stir-fry until the sauce is slightly reduced, about 1 minute longer.

3 Return the chicken to the skillet and stir-fry until heated through, about 1 minute. Serve with the rice.

PER SERVING (1½ cups chicken mixture and 1 cup rice): 455 Cal, 8 g Fat, 2 g Sat Fat, 0 g Trans Fat, 68 mg Chol, 1012 mg Sod, 62 g Carb, 10 g Fib, 33 g Prot, 75 mg Calc. *POINTS* value: *9.*

cumin, salt,
t the air and
g the bag

- 2 teaspoons olive oil
- 2 garlic cloves, minced
- 1 teaspoon ground cumin
- ¾ teaspoon salt
- ⅛ teaspoon cayenne
- 1 red onion, quartered and separated into leaves
- 1 cup whole-wheat couscous
- 3 tablespoons chopped fresh cilantro
- 2 teaspoons sesame seeds, toasted

2 Spray a nonstick ridged grill pan with nonstick spray and set over medium-high heat. Alternately thread the chicken and onion on 8 (12-inch) metal skewers. Place the skewers on the pan and cook, until the chicken is browned and cooked through, about 5 minutes on each side.

3 Meanwhile, prepare the couscous according to the package directions, omitting the fat and salt if desired. Sprinkle with the cilantro and sesame seeds. Serve with the chicken.

PER SERVING (2 skewers and ¾ cup couscous): 289 Cal, 8 g Fat, 2 g Sat Fat, 0 g Trans Fat, 68 mg Chol, 835 mg Sod, 26 g Carb, 5 g Fib, 30 g Prot, 48 mg Calc. *POINTS* value: *6.*

Filling Extra

For a quick side dish, thinly slice a zucchini and a yellow squash lengthwise and lightly spray with nonstick spray. Grill alongside along the chicken skewers until browned and tender.

Chicken Tikka with Cucumber Raita

PREP 15 MIN | **BROIL** 10 MIN | **SERVES** 4

- **1 cup plain fat-free yogurt**
- **Juice of ½ lemon**
- **2 garlic cloves, peeled**
- **1 (1-inch) piece fresh ginger, peeled and thinly sliced**
- **¾ teaspoon salt**
- **½ teaspoon garam masala**
- **½ teaspoon ground coriander**
- **½ teaspoon turmeric**
- **¼ teaspoon sugar**
- **Pinch cayenne**
- **1¼ pounds skinless boneless chicken breasts, cut into 1-inch pieces**
- **1 cucumber, finely diced**
- **¼ cup chopped fresh mint**
- **Pappadam or other flatbread, toasted (optional)**

1 Combine ⅓ cup of the yogurt, the lemon juice, garlic, ginger, ½ teaspoon of the salt, the garam masala, coriander, turmeric, sugar, and cayenne in a food processor and puree. Transfer the mixture to a large zip-close plastic bag and add the chicken. Squeeze out the air and seal the bag; turn to coat the chicken. Refrigerate, turning the bag occasionally, at least 30 minutes or up to overnight.

2 Preheat the broiler. Line a baking sheet with foil and spray with nonstick spray.

3 Remove the chicken from the marinade; discard the marinade. Thread the chicken on 8 (12-inch) metal skewers. Place the skewers on the prepared baking sheet. Broil 5 inches from the heat until the chicken is browned and cooked through, about 4 minutes on each side.

4 Meanwhile, to make the raita, stir together the remaining ⅔ cup yogurt, the cucumber, mint, and the remaining ¼ teaspoon salt in a serving bowl. Serve the raita with the chicken and pappadam, if using.

PER SERVING (2 skewers and ⅓ cup raita without pappadam): 181 Cal, 3 g Fat, 1 g Sat Fat, 0 g Trans Fat, 79 mg Chol, 461 mg Sod, 6 g Carb, 1 g Fib, 31 g Prot, 90 mg Calc. ***POINTS* value: *4.***

CHICKEN TIKKA WITH CUCUMBER RAITA

Turkey Cutlets with Orange Sauce

PREP 10 MIN | **COOK** 10 MIN | **SERVES** 4

- **4 (¼-pound) turkey cutlets**
- **2 teaspoons olive oil**
- **½ teaspoon salt**
- **¼ teaspoon black pepper**
- **1 shallot, minced**
- **2 teaspoons grated orange zest**
- **⅓ cup orange juice**
- **⅓ cup reduced-sodium chicken broth**
- **1 tablespoon cornstarch**
- **2 tablespoons chopped fresh chives**

1 Place the turkey cutlets between 2 pieces of plastic wrap. With a meat mallet or the bottom of a heavy saucepan, pound to ¼-inch thickness.

2 Heat the oil in a large nonstick skillet over medium-high heat. Sprinkle the turkey with the salt and pepper. Add the cutlets to the skillet and cook until lightly browned and cooked through, about 2 minutes on each side. Transfer to a plate and keep warm.

3 Reduce the heat to medium and add the shallot to the skillet. Cook, stirring, until softened, about 2 minutes.

4 Whisk together the orange zest and juice, broth, and cornstarch in a cup until smooth. Add the cornstarch mixture to the skillet and cook, stirring, until the sauce thickens and bubbles, about 2 minutes.

5 Return the turkey to the skillet. Cover and cook until heated through, about 1 minute longer. Sprinkle with the chives.

PER SERVING (1 turkey cutlet and 2½ tablespoons sauce): 166 Cal, 3 g Fat, 1 g Sat Fat, 0 g Trans Fat, 75 mg Chol, 347 mg Sod, 5 g Carb, 0 g Fib, 28 g Prot, 20 mg Calc. ***POINTS*** **value: *4*.**

Filling Extra

Serve this festive dish with baked sweet potatoes and steamed green beans (1 baked large sweet potato and 1 cup steamed green beans per serving will increase the *POINTS* value by *3*).

Salmon au Poivre with Watercress

PREP 10 MIN | **COOK** 10 MIN | **SERVES** 4

- **4 (6-ounce) skinless salmon fillets**
- **1 tablespoon mixed peppercorns, coarsely crashed**
- **¾ teaspoon salt**
- **3 bunches watercress, trimmed**
- **¼ red onion, thinly sliced**
- **1½ tablespoons lemon juice**
- **2 teaspoons sesame seeds, toasted (optional)**

1 Sprinkle the salmon evenly with the peppercorns and ½ teaspoon of the salt.

2 Spray a large nonstick skillet with nonstick spray and set over medium-high heat. Add the salmon and cook until lightly browned and just opaque in the center, about 4 minutes on each side.

3 Meanwhile, toss together the watercress, onion, lemon juice, sesame seeds, if using, and the remaining ¼ teaspoon salt in a large bowl. Lightly spray with olive oil nonstick spray and toss again. Divide the watercress salad evenly among 4 plates and top each serving with a piece of salmon.

PER SERVING (1 salmon fillet and 1½ cups salad without sesame seeds): 266 Cal, 11 g Fat, 2 g Sat Fat, 0 g Trans Fat, 94 mg Chol, 543 mg Sod, 3 g Carb, 1 g Fib, 37 g Prot, 101 mg Calc. *POINTS* value: *6.*

In the Kitchen

Before cooking the salmon, it's best to run your fingers lightly over its surface to check for any small bones that may be embedded in the flesh. If you find any, use clean tweezers or needle-nose pliers to pull them out.

SALMON PATTIES WITH CHUNKY TOMATO RELISH

Salmon Patties with Chunky Tomato Relish

PREP 15 MIN | **COOK** 10 MIN | **SERVES** 4

- **2 large tomatoes, preferably heirloom, seeded and coarsely chopped**
- **¼ cup chopped fresh basil**
- **2 shallots, finely chopped + 1 shallot, halved**
- **2 teaspoons lemon juice**
- **2 teaspoons olive oil**
- **¾ teaspoon salt**
- **½ teaspoon black pepper**
- **1 pound skinless salmon fillet, skinned and cut into small pieces**
- **2 tablespoons chopped fresh parsley**
- **1 teaspoon grated lemon zest**

1 To make the relish, toss together the tomatoes, basil, the chopped shallots, lemon juice, oil, and ¼ teaspoon each of the salt and pepper in a serving bowl.

2 To make the salmon patties, combine the salmon, parsley, the halved shallot, lemon zest, and the remaining ½ teaspoon salt and ¼ teaspoon pepper in a food processor; pulse until finely chopped. With damp hands, form the salmon mixture into 4 (½-inch-thick) patties

3 Spray a large nonstick skillet with olive oil nonstick spray and set over medium-high heat. Add the patties and cook until browned and cooked through, about 4 minutes on each side. Serve with the relish.

PER SERVING **(1 patty and about ½ cup relish): 214 Cal, 9 g Fat, 2 g Sat Fat, 0 g Trans Fat, 75 mg Chol, 518 mg Sod, 7 g Carb, 2 g Fib, 26 g Prot, 38 mg Calc.** ***POINTS*** **value:** ***5.***

Tip

This recipe works with the Simply Filling technique.

Tuna Steaks with Avocado-Orange Relish

PREP 10 MIN | **BROIL** 10 MIN | **SERVES** 4

- **2 teaspoons canola oil**
- **2 teaspoons reduced-sodium soy sauce**
- **4 (5-ounce) tuna steaks**
- **1 tablespoon red-wine vinegar**
- **2 teaspoons flaxseed oil**
- **1½ teaspoons minced peeled fresh ginger**
- **¼ teaspoon salt**
- **½ avocado, halved, pitted, peeled, and diced**
- **1 (11-ounce) can unsweetened mandarin orange sections, drained**
- **¼ small red onion, chopped**

1 Spray the broiler rack with nonstick spray and preheat the broiler.

2 Whisk together the canola oil and soy sauce in a small bowl. Brush the mixture on both sides of the tuna. Place the steaks on the broiler rack and broil 5 inches from the heat, about 3 minutes on each side for medium or until the desired doneness.

3 Meanwhile, to make the relish, whisk together the vinegar, flaxseed oil, ginger, and salt in a medium bowl. Add the avocado, orange sections, and onion; toss to coat. Serve with the tuna.

PER SERVING (1 tuna steak and ½ cup relish): 259 Cal, 9 g Fat, 1 g Sat Fat, 0 g Trans Fat, 66 mg Chol, 303 mg Sod, 8 g Carb, 2 g Fib, 35 g Prot, 32 mg Calc. *POINTS* value: *6.*

In the Kitchen

Flaxseed oil is rich in vitamin E and Omega 3s, so it's a good ingredient to work into your diet. Keep in mind that it shouldn't be exposed to high temperatures, so reserve it for salads and other uncooked dishes. This recipe works with the Simply Filling technique.

Roast Halibut with Chunky Roasted Pepper Sauce

PREP 15 MIN | **COOK** 10 MIN | **SERVES** 4

- **1 (12-ounce) jar roasted red pepper, drained and chopped**
- **16 pitted black and/or green olives, coarsely chopped**
- **¼ cup chopped fresh basil**
- **1 tablespoon sherry or red-wine vinegar**
- **1 tablespoon drained capers, coarsely chopped**
- **1 garlic clove, minced**
- **4 (6-ounce) halibut steaks, about ¾ inch thick**
- **2 teaspoons olive oil**
- **½ teaspoon salt**
- **¼ teaspoon black pepper**

1 Preheat the oven to 425°F. Spray a shallow roasting pan with nonstick spray.

2 To make the sauce, toss together the roasted red pepper, olives, basil, vinegar, capers, and garlic in a serving bowl.

3 Place the halibut in the prepared roasting pan; brush with the oil and sprinkle with the salt and black pepper. Roast the fish until just opaque in the center, about 10 minutes. Serve with the sauce.

PER SERVING (1 halibut steak and about ⅓ cup sauce): 215 Cal, 6 g Fat, 1 g Sat Fat, 0 g Trans Fat, 90 mg Chol, 806 mg Sod, 6 g Carb, 1 g Fib, 33 g Prot, 48 mg Calc. *POINTS* value: *5.*

Filling Extra

Add a 15½-ounce can of rinsed and drained cannellini (white kidney) beans to the roasted pepper sauce. This will increase the per-serving ***POINTS*** value by ***1.*** This recipe works with the Simply Filling technique.

FOUR-VEGETABLE
STIR-FRY WITH TOFU

Four-Vegetable Stir-Fry with Tofu

PREP 10 MIN | **COOK** 15 MIN | **SERVES** 4

- **1** **cup quick-cooking brown rice**
- **2** **teaspoons canola oil**
- **2** **garlic cloves, minced**
- **2** **teaspoons minced peeled fresh ginger**
- **12** **shiitake mushrooms, stems removed and caps thickly sliced**
- **3** **cups broccoli florets**
- **2** **carrots, thinly sliced**
- **1** **red bell pepper, thinly sliced**
- **1** **(14-ounce) container firm tofu, drained and diced**
- **2** **tablespoons reduced-sodium soy sauce**
- **1** **teaspoon dark (Asian) sesame oil**

1 Cook the rice according to the package directions, omitting the salt if desired.

2 Meanwhile, heat a large deep nonstick skillet or wok or over high heat until a drop of water sizzles in the pan. Add the canola oil and swirl to coat the skillet. Add the garlic and ginger and stir-fry until fragrant, about 30 seconds.

3 Add the mushrooms, broccoli, carrots, and bell pepper; stir-fry until tender, about 6 minutes. Add the remaining ingredients and stir-fry until heated through, about 1 minute longer. Serve with the rice.

PER SERVING (1¾ cups vegetable mixture and ½ cup rice): 267 Cal, 9 g Fat, 1 g Sat Fat, 0 g Trans Fat, 0 mg Chol, 754 mg Sod, 38 g Carb, 8 g Fib, 14 g Prot, 251 mg Calc. *POINTS* value: *5.*

Beef and Bean Soft Tacos

PREP 20 MIN | **COOK** 4–5 HRS ON HIGH OR 8–10 HRS ON LOW | **SERVES** 6

- **1½ cups reduced-sodium beef broth**
- **1 teaspoon chili powder**
- **1 (1-pound) flank steak, trimmed**
- **¾ cup chunky tomato salsa + additional for serving (optional)**
- **½ cup rinsed and drained canned black beans**
- **¼ cup fresh cilantro leaves**
- **2 tablespoons canned chopped mild green chiles, drained**
- **12 (7-inch) flour tortillas, warmed**
- **¼ cup fat-free sour cream**

1 Whisk together the broth and chili powder in a 5- or 6-quart slow cooker. Add the steak. Cover and cook until the steak is fork-tender, 4–5 hours on high or 8–10 hours on low.

2 Transfer the steak to a cutting board; discard all but ¼ cup of the cooking liquid; wipe out the slow cooker. With two forks, finely shred the beef. Return the beef to the slow cooker and stir in the reserved cooking liquid, ¾ cup of the salsa, the beans, cilantro, and chiles. Cook on high until heated through, about 5 minutes.

3 Top each tortilla evenly with the beef, salsa mixture, and sour cream. Fold the tortillas in half and serve with the additional salsa on the side, if using.

PER SERVING (2 tacos without additional salsa): 274 Cal, 5 g Fat, 1 g Sat Fat, 0 g Trans Fat, 56 mg Chol, 373 mg Sod, 30 g Carb, 5 g Fib, 28 g Prot, 78 mg Calc. *POINTS* value: *5.*

Filling Extra

Line each taco with some baby spinach or finely shredded green cabbage.

BEEF AND BEAN
SOFT TACOS

Low-and-Slow Sloppy Joes

PREP 20 MIN | **COOK** 3–4 HRS ON HIGH OR 6–8 HRS ON LOW | **SERVES** 6

- **1** **pound ground lean beef (7% fat or less)**
- **1** **(14½-ounce) can diced tomatoes**
- **1** **small onion, chopped**
- **1** **celery stalk, chopped**
- **3** **tablespoons packed dark brown sugar**
- **2** **teaspoons Worcestershire sauce**
- **1½** **teaspoons ground cumin**
- **1** **teaspoon chili powder**
- **½** **teaspoon salt**
- **6** **whole-wheat sandwich or hamburger rolls, split**

1 Spray a large nonstick skillet with nonstick spray and set over medium-high heat. Add the beef and cook, breaking it apart with a wooden spoon, until browned, about 5 minutes.

2 Transfer the beef to a 5- or 6-quart slow cooker. Stir in all the remaining ingredients except the rolls. Cover and cook until the flavors are blended and the sauce is slightly thickened, 3–4 hours on high or 6–8 hours on low.

3 Spoon ½ cup of the beef mixture into each roll.

PER SERVING (1 sandwich): 239 Cal, 6 g Fat, 2 g Sat Fat, 0 g Trans Fat, 43 mg Chol, 526 mg Sod, 26 g Carb, 4 g Fib, 20 g Prot, 83 mg Calc. *POINTS* value: *4.*

Filling Extra

To dress-up your "Joes," top each sandwich with a handful of shredded carrot or lettuce—or both.

Lamb and Vegetable Stew

PREP 25 MIN | **COOK** 4–6 HRS ON HIGH OR 8–10 HRS ON LOW | **SERVES** 4

- **2 teaspoons olive oil**
- **3 red onions, thinly sliced**
- **1 (24-ounce) package frozen stew vegetables, thawed**
- **1 pound boneless leg of lamb, trimmed and cut into 1-inch chunks**
- **2 cups reduced-sodium vegetable broth**
- **¾ teaspoon dried thyme**
- **½ teaspoon salt**
- **¼ teaspoon black pepper**

1 Heat the oil in a large nonstick skillet over medium heat. Add the onions and cook, stirring, until softened, about 8 minutes.

2 Transfer the onions to a 5- or 6-quart slow cooker and stir in the remaining ingredients. Cover and cook until the lamb and vegetables are fork-tender, 4–6 hours on high or 8–10 hours on low.

PER SERVING (2 cups): 340 Cal, 11 g Fat, 3 g Sat Fat, 0 g Trans Fat, 78 mg Chol, 534 mg Sod, 32 g Carb, 6 g Fib, 30 g Prot, 82 mg Calc. *POINTS* value: *7.*

Filling Extra

Add 2 cups frozen peas about 20 minutes before the cooking time is up and increase the per-serving *POINTS* value by *1.* This recipe works with the Simply Filling technique.

PORK MARRAKESH

Pork Marrakesh

PREP 25 MIN | **COOK** 3–4 HRS ON HIGH OR 6–8 HRS ON LOW | **SERVES** 4

- **2 teaspoons olive oil**
- **4 (¼-pound) boneless pork chops, trimmed**
- **¾ teaspoon salt**
- **¼ teaspoon black pepper**
- **3 small red onions, thinly sliced**
- **12 dried apricots, sliced**
- **¾ cup unsweetened apple juice**
- **2 teaspoons minced peeled fresh ginger**
- **½ teaspoon dried thyme**
- **1 (3-inch) cinnamon stick**
- **¼ cup chopped fresh cilantro**

1 Heat 1 teaspoon of the oil in a large nonstick skillet over medium-high heat. Sprinkle the pork chops with ¼ teaspoon of the salt and the pepper. Add the chops to the skillet and cook until browned, about 2 minutes on each side. Transfer to a plate.

2 Reduce the heat to medium and add the onions, the remaining 1 teaspoon oil, and the remaining ½ teaspoon salt to the skillet. Cook, stirring, until the onions are golden, about 10 minutes.

3 Place half of the apricots and half of the onions in the bottom of a 5- or 6-quart slow cooker. Top with the pork chops and the remaining onions and apricots. Add the apple juice, ginger, thyme, and cinnamon stick. Cover and cook until the pork is fork-tender, 3–4 hours on high or 6–8 hours on low. Remove the cinnamon stick and serve sprinkled with the cilantro.

PER SERVING (1 pork chop and ½ cup onion mixture): 281 Cal, 11 g Fat, 3 g Sat Fat, 0 g Trans Fat, 73 mg Chol, 492 mg Sod, 18 g Carb, 2 g Fib, 27 g Prot, 32 mg Calc. *POINTS* value: *6.*

Filling Extra

Couscous is ideal for soaking up all the great sauce (⅔ cup cooked whole-wheat couscous per serving will increase the *POINTS* value by *2*).

Braised Chicken in Riesling

PREP 25 MIN | **COOK** 4–6 HRS ON HIGH OR 8–10 HRS ON LOW | **SERVES** 6

- **6 skinless chicken thighs, trimmed**
- **½ teaspoon salt**
- **¼ teaspoon black pepper**
- **1 tablespoon olive oil**
- **1½ cups finely shredded green cabbage**
- **1 onion, thinly sliced**
- **1 cup baby-cut carrots**
- **3 garlic cloves, peeled**
- **¾ cup Riesling or other dry white wine**
- **¾ cup reduced-sodium chicken broth**
- **2 tablespoons tomato paste**
- **⅓ cup water**
- **2 tablespoons all-purpose flour**

1 Sprinkle the chicken with the salt and pepper.

2 Heat the oil in a large nonstick skillet over medium-high heat. Add the chicken and cook, turning, until browned, about 8 minutes. Transfer the chicken to a 5- or 6-quart slow cooker.

3 Add the cabbage and onion to the skillet. Reduce the heat to medium and cook, stirring, until the onion is softened, about 5 minutes. Transfer to the slow cooker and top with the carrots and garlic.

4 Whisk together the wine, broth, and tomato paste in a bowl, then pour over the chicken. Cover and cook until the chicken and carrots are fork-tender, 4–6 hours on high or 8–10 hours on low. With a slotted spoon, transfer the chicken to a deep platter. Keep warm.

5 Whisk together the water and flour in a small bowl until smooth. Whisk in about 1/4 cup of the hot stew liquid until blended, then stir the flour mixture into the slow cooker. Cover and cook on high until the mixture simmers and thickens, about 15 minutes longer. Serve over the chicken.

PER SERVING (1 chicken thigh and ½ cup vegetables with sauce): 175 Cal, 8 g Fat, 2 g Sat Fat, 0 g Trans Fat, 43 mg Chol, 365 mg Sod, 9 g Carb, 2 g Fib, 16 g Prot, 43 mg Calc. *POINTS* value: *4.*

In the Kitchen

This dish is traditionally made with a dry red wine, but it is lighter and equally delicious made with a white wine such as Riesling. If you prefer not to use wine, substitute an equal amount of reduced-sodium chicken broth.

Chicken and Vegetable Curry

PREP 25 MIN | **COOK** 4–6 HRS ON HIGH OR 8–10 HRS ON LOW | **SERVES** 5

- **2 teaspoons olive oil**
- **2 large onions, thinly sliced**
- **1 teaspoon garam masala or curry powder**
- **1 pound skinless boneless chicken breasts, cut into 1-inch pieces**
- **3 small sweet potatoes, peeled, halved lengthwise, and cut into ½-inch slices**
- **1½ cups reduced-sodium chicken broth**
- **½ teaspoon salt**
- **¼ teaspoon cayenne**
- **1 cup brown rice, preferably basmati**
- **1 (16-ounce) bag frozen broccoli, cauliflower, and carrots, thawed**

1 Heat the oil in a large nonstick skillet over medium heat. Add the onions and cook, stirring, until softened, about 6 minutes. Remove the skillet from the heat and stir in the garam masala.

2 Transfer the onions to a 5- or 6-quart slow cooker and add the chicken and potatoes.

3 Stir together the broth, salt, and cayenne in a large glass measure or bowl, then stir into the chicken mixture. Cover and cook until the chicken and potatoes are fork-tender, 4–6 hours on high or 8–10 hours on low.

4 Meanwhile, cook the rice according to the package directions, omitting the salt if desired.

5 About 20 minutes before the cooking time is up, add the vegetables to the slow cooker. Cover and cook on high until the vegetables are crisp-tender, about 20 minutes longer.

6 Divide the rice evenly among 4 bowls and top with the curry.

PER SERVING (1¾ cups curry and ½ cup rice): 353 Cal, 6 g Fat, 1 g Sat Fat, 0 g Trans Fat, 55 mg Chol, 834 mg Sod, 47 g Carb, 9 g Fib, 27 g Prot, 80 mg Calc. *POINTS* value: *7.*

Tip

This recipe works with the Simply Filling technique.

Easy Chicken Gumbo

PREP 25 MIN | **COOK** 4–6 HRS ON HIGH OR 8–10 HRS ON LOW | **SERVES** 4

- **1 tablespoon olive oil**
- **2 onions, thinly sliced**
- **4 skinless boneless chicken thighs, trimmed and cut into chunks**
- **3 cups thawed frozen or fresh okra**
- **1 (14½-ounce) can petite diced tomatoes**
- **5 celery stalks with leaves, sliced**
- **3 garlic cloves, peeled**
- **1½ cups reduced-sodium chicken broth**
- **1 teaspoon dried thyme**
- **½ teaspoon salt**
- **¼ teaspoon cayenne**
- **2 teaspoons gumbo filé powder**
- **2 cups hot cooked brown rice**

1 Heat the oil in a large nonstick skillet over medium-high heat. Add the onions and cook, stirring, until softened, about 5 minutes.

2 Transfer the onions to a 5- or 6-quart slow cooker and stir in the chicken, okra, tomatoes, celery, and garlic.

3 Whisk together the broth, thyme, salt, and cayenne in a large glass measure and add to the slow cooker. Cover and cook until the chicken is fork-tender, 4–6 hours on high or 8–10 hours on low. Discard the garlic. Turn off the slow cooker and stir in the filé powder. Cover and let stand until the flavors are blended, about 10 minutes.

4 Divide the rice evenly among 4 bowls and top with the gumbo.

PER SERVING (1 cup gumbo and ½ cup rice): 343 Cal, 10 g Fat, 2 g Sat Fat, 0 g Trans Fat, 43 mg Chol, 1037 mg Sod, 43 g Carb, 7 g Fib, 23 g Prot, 243 mg Calc. *POINTS* value: *7.*

In the Kitchen

Filé powder, used to thicken gumbo and other Creole dishes in New Orleans, is made from the ground dried leaves of the sassafras tree. It is always stirred into a dish after it is removed from the heat, otherwise it will become stringy. This recipe works with the Simply Filling technique.

EASY CHICKEN GUMBO

Vegetarian Burritos with Salsa Verde

PREP 15 MIN | **COOK** 3–4 HRS ON HIGH OR 6–8 HRS ON LOW | **SERVES** 8

- **1 (14½-ounce) can fire-roasted diced tomatoes**
- **2 (15½-ounce) cans black beans, rinsed and drained**
- **1 (8¾-ounce) can corn kernels, drained**
- **3 tablespoons taco or Mexican seasoning**
- **2 cups lightly packed sliced Swiss chard**
- **8 (7-inch) whole-wheat tortillas, warmed**
- **1 cup reduced-fat pepper Jack cheese**
- **½ cup fat-free sour cream**
- **½ cup salsa verde**

1 Drain the tomatoes and reserve all but ½ cup of the liquid. Put the tomatoes and the reserved liquid in a 5- or 6-quart slow cooker. Add the beans, corn, and taco seasoning. Cover and cook until the flavors are blended, 3–4 hours on high or 6–8 hours on low.

2 About 20 minutes before the cooking time is up, stir in the Swiss chard. Coarsely mash the bean mixture with a potato masher or wooden spoon.

3 Lay the tortillas out on a work surface. Spoon ½ cup of the bean mixture on each tortilla. Top evenly with the pepper Jack, sour cream, and salsa verde. Roll up the tortillas to enclose the filling.

PER SERVING (1 burrito): 271 Cal, 5 g Fat, 2 g Sat Fat, 0 g Trans Fat, 11 mg Chol, 948 mg Sod, 45 g Carb, 12 g Fib, 14 g Prot, 210 mg Calc. *POINTS* value: *5.*

Filling Extra

Double the amount of Swiss chard—you'll also be getting more fiber, vitamins, and antioxidants.

Beef, Beet, and Cabbage Soup

PREP 30 MIN | **COOK** 4–6 HRS ON HIGH OR 8–10 HRS ON LOW | **SERVES** 8

- **2 teaspoons olive oil**
- **1 pound boneless chuck, trimmed and cut into ¾-inch pieces**
- **2 onions, thinly sliced**
- **4 beets, trimmed, peeled, and diced**
- **3 carrots, sliced**
- **1 cup thinly sliced green cabbage**
- **1 (14½-ounce) can petite diced tomatoes**
- **½ teaspoon salt**
- **¼ teaspoon black pepper**
- **1 bay leaf**
- **8 cups reduced-sodium beef broth**

1 Heat the oil in a large nonstick skillet over medium-high heat. Add the beef, in batches, and cook, stirring, until browned, about 8 minutes. Transfer the beef to a 5- or 6-quart slow cooker.

2 Add the onions to the skillet and cook, stirring, until softened, about 5 minutes. Add to the slow cooker along with the remaining ingredients. Cover and cook until the beef and vegetables are fork-tender, 4–6 hours on high or 8–10 hours on low.

3 Remove the bay leaf. Ladle the soup evenly into 6 bowls.

PER SERVING (about 1⅓ cups): 197 Cal, 9 g Fat, 3 g Sat Fat, 0 g Trans Fat, 29 mg Chol, 474 mg Sod, 14 g Carb, 3 g Fib, 16 g Prot, 53 mg Calc. *POINTS* value: *4.*

VEGETABLE MINESTRONE
WITH PASTA

Vegetable Minestrone with Pasta

PREP 25 MIN | **COOK** 4–5 HRS ON HIGH OR 8–10 HRS ON LOW | **SERVES** 6

- **1 (15½-ounce) can chickpeas, rinsed and drained**
- **1 (14½-ounce) can petite diced tomatoes**
- **2 carrots, sliced**
- **2 onions, diced**
- **2 celery stalks with leaves, sliced**
- **1 small zucchini, halved lenghtwise and sliced**
- **1 small yellow squash, halved lengthwise and sliced**
- **½ pound green beans, trimmed and cut into 1-inch pieces**
- **2 garlic cloves, chopped**
- **½ teaspoon salt**
- **¼ teaspoon black pepper**
- **7 cups water**
- **1½ cups whole-wheat spirals or other tube pasta**
- **¼ cup chopped fresh basil or flat-leaf parsley**

1 Combine all the ingredients except the pasta and basil in a 5- or 6-quart slow cooker. Cover and cook until the vegetables are fork-tender, 4–5 hours on high or 8–10 hours on low.

2 About 30 minutes before the cooking time is up, cook the macaroni according to the package directions, omitting the salt if desired. Stir the pasta and basil into the soup.

PER SERVING (about 2 cups): 247 Cal, 2 g Fat, 0 g Sat Fat, 0 g Trans Fat, 0 mg Chol, 408 mg Sod, 50 g Carb, 9 g Fib, 12 g Prot, 111 mg Calc. *POINTS* value: *4.*

Filling Extra

Add 2 Yukon Gold potatoes, peeled and diced, to the soup at the same time as the other vegetables. This will increase the per-serving *POINTS* value by *1.* This recipe works with the Simply Filling technique.

Blueberries with Whipped Ricotta and Balsamic Syrup

PREP 10 MIN | **COOK** 5 MIN | **SERVES** 4

- **¼ cup balsamic vinegar**
- **1 cup fat-free ricotta cheese**
- **4 teaspoons sugar**
- **2 teaspoons grated orange zest**
- **2 pints blueberries**
- **Orange zest strips**

1 Bring the vinegar to a boil in a medium saucepan over medium heat; boil until reduced by half, about 2 minutes. Remove the saucepan from the heat and let cool about 5 minutes.

2 Meanwhile, puree the ricotta in a mini– or regular food processor. Scrape the cheese into a small bowl and stir in the sugar and orange zest.

3 Divide the blueberries evenly among 4 dessert dishes; top evenly with the ricotta mixture. Drizzle evenly with the vinegar and sprinkle with the zest strips.

PER SERVING (½ cup blueberries and ¼ cup ricotta): 153 Cal, 1 g Fat, 0 g Sat Fat, 0 g Trans Fat, 10 mg Chol, 76 mg Sod, 30 g Carb, 6 g Fib, 6 g Prot, 133 mg Calc. *POINTS* value: *2.*

BLUEBERRIES WITH WHIPPED RICOTTA AND BALSAMIC SYRUP

Frozen Strawberry-Maple Yogurt

PREP 20 MIN | **COOK** NONE | **SERVES** 8

- **1 (1-pound) container strawberries, hulled and chopped**
- **1 cup sugar**
- **2 tablespoons lemon juice**
- **1 cup maple or vanilla low-fat yogurt**
- **1 cup fat-free half-and-half**
- **½ teaspoon maple extract**

1 Stir together the strawberries, sugar, and lemon juice in a medium bowl; let stand 30 minutes.

2 Whisk together the remaining ingredients in a large bowl. Stir in the strawberry mixture. Cover and refrigerate until thoroughly chilled, at least 2 hours or up to overnight.

3 Pour the strawberry mixture into an ice-cream maker and freeze according to the manufacturer's instructions.

4 Transfer the yogurt to a freezer container and freeze until firm, at least 2 hours or up to 6 hours.

PER SERVING (½ cup): 159 Cal, 1 g Fat, 1 g Sat Fat, 0 g Trans Fat, 3 mg Chol, 100 mg Sod, 37 g Carb, 1 g Fib, 3 g Prot, 91 mg Calc. *POINTS* value: *3.*

Frozen Vanilla Yogurt with Sugared Shredded Wheat

PREP 15 MIN | **BAKE** 15 MIN | **SERVES** 4

- **2** **original-size shredded wheat**
- **1** **tablespoon unsalted butter, melted**
- **1** **tablespoon sugar**
- **1** **pint frozen vanilla low-fat yogurt or other favorite flavor**
- **2** **cups mixed berries**

1 Preheat the oven to 400°F.

2 Break each piece of shredded wheat crosswise into quarters and place in a medium bowl. Drizzle with the butter and toss to coat. Sprinkle with the sugar and toss to coat.

3 Arrange the shredded wheat in one layer on a baking sheet. Bake until deep golden brown, about 15 minutes. Let cool about 5 minutes on the baking sheet.

4 Place ½-cup scoop of the yogurt in each of 4 dessert dishes. Divide the berries evenly among the dishes. Coarsely crumble the shredded wheat and pile on top of the yogurt.

PER SERVING (½ cup yogurt, ½ shredded wheat, and ½ cup berries): 242 Cal, 5 g Fat, 3 g Sat Fat, 0 g Trans Fat, 15 mg Chol, 78 mg Sod, 44 g Carb, 3 g Fib, 7 g Prot, 209 mg Calc. *POINTS* value: *5.*

Vanilla Yogurt Sundae

PREP 5 MIN | **COOK** NONE | **SERVES** 1

- **1** **(½-cup) scoop frozen vanilla fat-free yogurt**
- **1** **tablespoon toasted wheat germ**
- **1** **tablespoon chopped walnuts**
- **2** **tablespoons thawed frozen fat-free whipped topping**
- **1** **fresh sweet or maraschino cherry**

Place the yogurt in a dessert dish. Top with the wheat germ, walnuts, whipped topping, and cherry.

PER SERVING (1 sundae): 181 Cal, 6 g Fat, 1 g Sat Fat, 0 g Trans Fat, 2 mg Chol, 65 mg Sod, 26 g Carb, 2 g Fib, 8 g Prot, 179 mg Calc. *POINTS* value: *4.*

Filling Extra

Turn this into a banana split by cutting half a banana lengthwise in half and placing it around the yogurt (½ large banana will increase the *POINTS* value by *1*).

Raspberry-Orange Sorbet

PREP 15 MIN | **COOK** 10 MIN | **SERVES** 8

- **2 cups water**
- **½ cup sugar**
- **2 (3-inch) strips orange zest, removed with a vegetable peeler**
- **3 tablespoons orange juice**
- **3½ cups fresh or thawed frozen raspberries**

1 To make the sugar syrup, combine the water, sugar, and orange zest in a medium saucepan and set over high heat. Bring to a boil, stirring until the sugar is dissolved. Reduce the heat and simmer 5 minutes. Remove the saucepan from the heat and let cool about 5 minutes. Discard the orange zest; stir in the orange juice.

2 Puree 1 cup of the sugar syrup with the raspberries in a food processor or blender. Stir the raspberry mixture into the sugar syrup in the saucepan. Pour the raspberry mixture through a sieve set over a medium bowl, pressing hard on the solids to extract as much liquid as possible. Discard the solids. Cover the berry mixture and refrigerate until thoroughly chilled, at least 2 hours or up to overnight.

3 Transfer the raspberry mixture to an ice-cream maker and freeze according to the manufacturer's instructions.

4 Transfer the sorbet to a freezer container and freeze until firm, at least 2 hours or up to 6 hours.

PER SERVING (about ½ cup): **90 Cal, 0 g Fat, 0 g Sat Fat, 0 g Trans Fat, 0 mg Chol, 44 mg Sod, 22 g Carb, 1 g Fib, 43 g Prot, 17 mg Calc.** *POINTS* value: *2.*

WHITE WINE–POACHED
PEARS

White Wine–Poached Pears

PREP 15 MIN | **COOK** 45 MIN | **SERVES** 8

- **4 cups water**
- **1 cup dry white wine**
- **1 cup sugar**
- **Zest of 1 lemon, removed in strips with a vegetable peeler**
- **1 tablespoon lemon juice**
- **4 large firm-ripe Bartlett or Bosc pears, peeled, halved, and cored**

1 Combine all the ingredients except the pears in a large saucepan and bring to a boil over high heat; boil 10 minutes.

2 Add the pears to the saucepan. Reduce the heat and gently simmer, covered, until the pears are tender when pierced with a fork, about 15 minutes. With a slotted spoon, carefully transfer the pears to a large shallow bowl.

3 Bring the poaching liquid to a boil over high heat; boil until reduced to about 2 cups, about 15 minutes. Discard the zest, if desired. Pour the poaching liquid over the pears and refrigerate until cool before serving.

PER SERVING (½ pear and ¼ cup syrup): **166 Cal, 0 g Fat, 0 g Sat Fat, 0 g Trans Fat, 0 mg Chol, 41 mg Sod, 42 g Carb, 3 g Fib, 0 g Prot, 17 mg Calc.** *POINTS* value: *3.*

In the Kitchen

You can also poach the pears in red wine, which gives the pears a pretty pink hue.

APRICOT AND TOASTED
ALMOND GALETTE

Apricot and Toasted Almond Galette

PREP 35 MIN | **BAKE** 20 MIN | **SERVES** 8

1⅓ cups all-purpose flour

½ cup + 2 tablespoons sugar

1 tablespoon baking powder

Pinch salt

⅓ cup part-skim ricotta cheese

2 tablespoons cold unsalted butter, cut into pieces

2 large egg whites

2 teaspoons water

2 pounds ripe apricots, halved, pitted, and cut into ½-inch wedges

2 tablespoons slivered almonds

1 To make the dough, combine the flour, ½ cup of the sugar, the baking powder, and salt in a food processor and pulse to mix. Add the ricotta, butter, 1 egg white, and the water to the food processor; pulse just until the dough begins to come together. Shape the dough into a disk and wrap in plastic wrap; refrigerate at least 1 hour or up to overnight.

2 Preheat the oven to 350°F. Lightly spray a large baking sheet with nonstick spray.

3 Roll out the dough between 2 sheets of wax paper to a form a 10-inch round. Place the dough on the prepared baking sheet. Fold the edge of the dough over to form a ½-inch rim. Bake for 10 minutes, then let cool on a wire rack about 5 minutes.

4 Lightly beat the remaining egg white and brush it over the crust. Arrange the apricots on the crust in concentric circles and sprinkle with the remaining 2 tablespoons sugar and the almonds. Bake until the crust is golden and the apricots are softened, about 20 minutes. Let cool slightly on a wire rack.

5 Cut into 8 wedges. Serve warm or at room temperature.

PER SERVING (1 wedge): 241 Cal, 5 g Fat, 2 g Sat Fat, 0 g Trans Fat, 11 mg Chol, 246 mg Sod, 45 g Carb, 2 g Fib, 5 g Prot, 145 mg Calc. *POINTS* **value:** *5.*

Peach-Blueberry Crostatas

PREP 30 MIN | **BAKE** 25 MIN | **SERVES** 8

- **½ cup whole-wheat pastry flour**
- **½ cup all-purpose flour**
- **½ teaspoon salt**
- **2 tablespoons cold unsalted butter, cut into pieces**
- **2 tablespoons canola oil**
- **2–4 tablespoons ice water**
- **2 ripe peaches, peeled, halved, pitted, and cut into ½-inch wedges**
- **1 cup blueberries**
- **3 tablespoons granulated sugar**
- **½ teaspoon lemon juice**
- **1 tablespoon fat-free milk**
- **2 teaspoons turbinado or granulated sugar**

1 Whisk together the whole-wheat flour, all-purpose flour, and salt in a medium bowl. With a pastry blender or 2 knives used scissor-fashion, cut in the butter and oil until the mixture resembles coarse crumbs. Gradually add the water to the flour mixture, tossing lightly until the pastry is just moist enough to hold together. Shape the dough into 4 equal disks. Wrap each disk in plastic wrap and refrigerate until chilled, at least 30 minutes or up to overnight.

2 Preheat the oven to 425°F. Line a large baking sheet with foil; spray with nonstick spray.

3 Toss together the peaches, blueberries, granulated sugar, and lemon juice in a medium bowl.

4 With a floured rolling pin, roll out each disk of dough on a sheet of floured wax paper to form a 6-inch round. Flip the dough onto the prepared baking sheet and peel away the wax paper. (If the dough tears, patch it together with your fingers.) Mound one-quarter of the fruit filling on each round, leaving a 1-inch border. Fold the rim of the dough over the filling, pleating it as you go around. Brush the crusts with the milk and sprinkle evenly with the turbinado sugar. Bake until the peaches are tender and the crust is browned, about 25 minutes. Let cool slightly on a wire rack.

5 Cut each crostata in half and serve warm or at room temperature.

PER SERVING (½ crostata): 158 Cal, 7 g Fat, 2 g Sat Fat, 0 g Trans Fat, 8 mg Chol, 150 mg Sod, 27 g Carb, 2 g Fib, 2 g Prot, 12 mg Calc. *POINTS* value: *3.*

PEACH-BLUEBERRY CROSTATAS

Microwave Apple-Pear Crisp

PREP 10 MIN | **MICROWAVE** 10 MIN | **SERVES** 6

- **2 Golden Delicious apples, peeled, halved, cored, and thinly sliced**
- **2 Bartlett pears, peeled, halved, cored, and thinly sliced**
- **¼ cup dried cherries or cranberries**
- **4 tablespoons packed light brown sugar**
- **¾ teaspoon cinnamon**
- **1 cup low-fat granola**
- **2 tablespoons butter, melted**

1 Spray a microwavable 8-inch square dish with nonstick spray.

2 Gently stir together the apples, pears, dried cherries, 3 tablespoons of the brown sugar, and ½ teaspoon of the cinnamon in a large bowl. Spread evenly in the baking dish.

3 Toss together the granola, butter, and the remaining 1 tablespoon brown sugar and ¼ teaspoon cinnamon in a small bowl. Sprinkle the granola mixture evenly over the fruit mixture. Microwave on High until the apples and pears are tender, about 8 minutes. Serve warm or at room temperature.

PER SERVING (⅙ of crisp): 202 Cal, 5 g Fat, 3 g Sat Fat, 0 g Trans Fat, 10 mg Chol, 72 mg Sod, 41 g Carb, 4 g Fib, 2 g Prot, 27 mg Calc. *POINTS* value: *4.*

Whole Grain and Fruit Oatmeal Cookies

PREP 25 MIN | **BAKE** 25 MIN | **MAKES** 36

- **1½ cups rolled (old-fashioned) oats**
- **½ cup whole-wheat flour**
- **½ cup toasted wheat germ**
- **½ cup low-fat granola**
- **¼ cup golden raisins**
- **¼ cup mini–semisweet chocolate chips**
- **2 tablespoons unsalted sunflower seeds**
- **2 tablespoons finely chopped dried apricots**
- **1 teaspoon baking powder**
- **½ teaspoon salt**
- **½ cup (1 stick) unsalted butter, softened**
- **½ cup packed brown sugar**
- **¼ cup water**
- **1 large egg**
- **1 teaspoon vanilla extract**

1 Preheat the oven to 375°F. Spray 2 large baking sheets with nonstick spray.

2 Toss together the oats, whole-wheat flour, wheat germ, granola, raisins, chocolate chips, sunflower seeds, apricots, baking powder, and salt in a large bowl.

3 With an electric mixer on medium speed, beat the butter and brown sugar until light and fluffy. Beat in the water, egg, and vanilla just until smooth. With a rubber spatula, stir in the flour mixture until combined.

4 Drop the dough by level measuring tablespoons, about 1 inch apart, onto the prepared baking sheets and flatten until 1½ inches in diameter. Bake until the cookies are golden brown and the edges are deep brown, 10–12 minutes.

5 Let the cookies cool slightly on the baking sheet on a wire rack. With a metal spatula, transfer the cookies to a wire rack to cool completely. Repeat with the remaining dough.

PER SERVING (1 cookie): 79 Cal, 4 g Fat, 2 g Sat Fat, 0 g Trans Fat, 13 mg Chol, 54 mg Sod, 10 g Carb, 1 g Fib, 2 g Prot, 17 mg Calc. *POINTS* value: *2.*

In the Kitchen

Using the same proportions, substitute your favorite toasted and chopped nuts for the sunflower seeds and/or a favorite dried fruit for the raisins and apricots. Try chopped dried sour cherries and pistachios or hazelnuts and dried peaches.

PUMPKIN-CRANBERRY BREAD PUDDING

Pumpkin-Cranberry Bread Pudding

PREP 30 MIN | **COOK/BAKE** 1 HR 20 MIN | **SERVES** 12

- **3 cups fat-free half-and-half**
- **1 cup fat-free egg substitute**
- **½ cup packed dark brown sugar**
- **1 teaspoon cinnamon**
- **¼ teaspoon nutmeg**
- **¼ teaspoon ground allspice**
- **¼ teaspoon salt**
- **1 cup canned pumpkin puree**
- **2 teaspoons vanilla extract**
- **1 (1-pound) loaf day-old whole-wheat bread, cut into 1½-inch pieces**
- **½ cup dried cranberries**
- **½ cup chopped pecans**

1 Bring the half-and-half to a boil in a medium saucepan over medium-high heat; remove the saucepan from the heat.

2 Whisk together the egg substitute, brown sugar, cinnamon, nutmeg, allspice, and salt in a medium bowl. Slowly add ½ cup of the hot half-and-half to the brown sugar mixture, whisking constantly.

3 Return the half-and-half mixture to the saucepan and set over medium-low heat. Cook, whisking constantly, until the custard thickens and coats the back of a spoon, about 5 minutes. Immediately pour the custard through a sieve set over a medium bowl. Whisk in the pumpkin and vanilla. Add the bread and cranberries, gently stirring until moistened. Let stand about 20 minutes.

4 Meanwhile, preheat the oven to 325°F. Spray 12(6-ounce) ramekins or a 10-cup baking dish or casserole with nonstick spray.

5 Spoon the pudding mixture into the prepared cups and sprinkle evenly with the pecans. Place the cups in a roasting pan. Add enough boiling water to the pan to come halfway up the sides of the cups. Cover tightly with foil. Bake single puddings 20 minutes and large pudding 1 hour. Uncover and bake until a knife inserted into the center comes out clean, 5–15 minutes longer. Serve warm or at room temperature.

PER SERVING (1/12 of bread pudding): 239 Cal, 5 g Fat, 1 g Sat Fat, 0 g Trans Fat, 3 mg Chol, 438 mg Sod, 41 g Carb, 2 g Fib, 8 g Prot, 143 mg Calc. *POINTS* value: *5.*

FROM TOP, CLOCKWISE
CHUNKY GUACAMOLE, BLACK BEAN –TOMATILLO DIP, PAGE 268, AND TOSTONES (FRIED GREEN PLANTAINS), PAGE 279

Chunky Guacamole

PREP 10 MIN | **COOK** NONE | **SERVES** 6

- **2** **Hass avocados, halved, pitted, and peeled**
- **1** **small tomato, seeded and chopped**
- **¼** **cup chopped fresh cilantro**
- **1½** **tablespoons lime or lemon juice**
- **¼** **cup finely chopped onion**
- **½** **teaspoon salt**
- **¼** **teaspoon black pepper**
- **4** **drops hot pepper sauce**

Coarsely mash the avocados in a medium bowl. Add the remaining ingredients and stir until combined. Serve at once or press a piece of plastic wrap directly onto the surface to prevent the guacamole from browning. Refrigerate up to 3 hours.

PER SERVING (2 tablespoons): 47 Cal, 4 g Fat, 1 g Sat Fat, 0 g Trans Fat, 0 mg Chol, 51 mg Sod, 3 g Carb, 2 g Fib, 1 g Prot, 4 mg Calc. *POINTS* value: *1.*

Tip

This recipe works with the Simply Filling technique.

Chili-Spiced Popcorn

PREP 10 MIN | **COOK** NONE | **SERVES** 6

- **6 cups plain air-popped popcorn**
- **1 tablespoon chili powder**
- **½ teaspoon paprika**
- **½ teaspoon onion powder**
- **½ teaspoon ground cumin**

Place the popcorn in a large bowl and spray with nonstick spray; toss to coat. Sprinkle the remaining ingredients over the popcorn and toss to coat evenly.

PER SERVING (1 cup): 36 Cal, 1 g Fat, 0 g Sat Fat, 0 g Trans Fat, 0 mg Chol, 14 mg Sod, 7 g Carb, 2 g Fib, 1 g Prot, 9 mg Calc. *POINTS* value: *0.*

Tip

This recipe works with the Simply Filling technique.

CHILI-SPICED POPCORN AND SMOKY PUMPKIN SEEDS, PAGE 278

Smoky Pumpkin Seeds

PREP 10 MIN | **BAKE** 15 MIN | **SERVES** 16

- **2 cups shelled pumpkin seeds (about 10 ounces)**
- **2 teaspoons Worcestershire sauce**
- **1 teaspoon liquid smoke**
- **1 teaspoon ground cumin**
- **1 teaspoon chili powder**
- **½ teaspoon salt**
- **½ teaspoon garlic powder**
- **⅛ teaspoon cayenne**

1 Preheat the oven to 325°F. Line a large baking sheet with parchment paper.

2 Toss together the pumpkin seeds, Worcestershire sauce, and liquid smoke in a large bowl.

3 Combine the remaining ingredients in a small bowl. Sprinkle the spice mixture over the pumpkin seeds and stir vigorously with a wooden spoon until evenly coated.

4 Spread the pumpkin seeds on the prepared baking sheet. Bake, stirring twice, until dried and lightly browned, about 15 minutes. Let cool on the baking sheet on a wire rack about 30 minutes.

PER SERVING (2 tablespoons): 152 Cal, 12 g Fat, 2 g Sat Fat, 0 g Trans Fat, 0 mg Chol, 160 mg Sod, 8 g Carb, 2 g Fib, 10 g Prot, 16 mg Calc. *POINTS* value: *4.*

In the Kitchen

These tasty pumpkin seeds, known as pepitas (peh-PEE-tahs) in Spanish, can be stored in a zip-close plastic bag or airtight container for up to 1 month.

Tostones (Fried Green Plantains)

PREP 10 MIN | **COOK** 15 MIN | **SERVES** 4

- **4 teaspoons olive oil**
- **2 (10-ounce) green plantains, peeled and cut on a diagonal into ½-inch slices (about 20 pieces)**
- **1 teaspoon salt**

1 Heat the oil in a large nonstick skillet over medium-high heat. Cook the plantains, in batches, until tender and golden brown, about 5 minutes on each side. Transfer the plantain slices to a double thickness of paper towels to drain. With the bottom of a heavy plate or saucepan, gently press down on the slices, one at a time, to flatten to 1/4-inch thickness.

2 Spray the same skillet with olive oil nonstick spray and set over medium-high heat. Add the plantain slices, in batches, and cook until nicely browned, about 1 minute on each side. Sprinkle with the salt while hot.

PER SERVING (about 5 pieces): 185 Cal, 3 g Fat, 0 Sat Fat, 0 g Trans Fat, 0 Chol, 153 mg Sod, 44 g Carb, 3 g Fiber, 1 g Prot, 4 mg Calc. *POINTS* value: *3.*

In the Kitchen

Here's how to peel a plantain: cut off both ends, then cut it crosswise in half. With a small knife, slit the skin along its ridges, cutting down to the flesh, then peel off the skin. This recipe works with the Simply Filling technique.

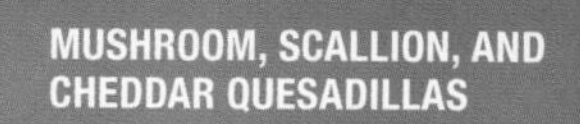

MUSHROOM, SCALLION, AND
CHEDDAR QUESADILLAS

Mushroom, Scallion, and Cheddar Quesadillas

PREP 10 MIN | **COOK** 20 MIN | **SERVES** 8

- **1** **(8-ounce) package sliced white mushrooms**
- **8** **(7-inch) fat-free whole-wheat flour tortillas**
- **¾** **cup shredded reduced-fat cheddar cheese**
- **2** **scallions, thinly sliced**
- **2** **tablespoons sliced pickled jalapeño peppers, drained and finely chopped**

1 Spray a large nonstick skillet with nonstick spray and set over medium heat. Add the mushrooms and cook, stirring occasionally, until the mushroom liquid is evaporated, about 6 minutes. With a slotted spoon, transfer the mushrooms to a plate and let cool slightly.

2 Lay 4 of the tortillas out on a work surface. Layer each with one-fourth of the mushrooms, cheddar, scallions, and jalapeños. Top with the remaining 4 tortillas, lightly pressing down.

3 Wipe the skillet clean. Spray with nonstick spray and set over medium heat. Cook the quesadillas, one at a time, the until crisp and the cheese begins to melt, about 1½ minutes on each side. Transfer to a cutting board and cover loosely with foil to keep warm. Cut each quesadilla into 4 wedges.

PER SERVING (2 wedges): 128 Cal, 1 g Fat, 1 g Sat Fat, 0 g Trans Fat, 2 mg Chol, 468 mg Sod, 23 g Carb, 4 g Fib, 8 g Prot, 124 mg Calc. *POINTS* value: *2.*

Filling Extra

Want more earthy mushroom flavor as well as a little more bulk? Use ¾ pound of mushrooms instead of ½ pound.

Shrimp-"Stuffed" Cucumber Slices

PREP 20 MIN | **COOK** NONE | **SERVES** 4

1 tablespoon + 1 teaspoon fat-free mayonnaise
1 tablespoon finely chopped celery
1 tablespoon finely chopped fresh chives
½ teaspoon grated lemon zest
2 teaspoons lemon juice
⅛ teaspoon salt
Few drops hot pepper sauce
¼ pound cooked peeled and deveined shrimp, finely chopped
1 English (seedless) cucumber, cut into 20 (½-inch) slices

Combine the mayonnaise, celery, chives, lemon zest and juice, salt, and pepper sauce in a medium bowl. Stir in the shrimp. Spoon about 1 teaspoon of the shrimp mixture onto each cucumber slice. Serve at once or cover and refrigerate for up to 2 hours.

PER SERVING (5 stuffed cucumber slices): 43 Cal, 0 g Fat, 0 g Sat Fat, 0 g Trans Fat, 30 mg Chol, 193 mg Sod, 3 g Carb, 0 g Fib, 5 g Prot, 43 mg Calc. *POINTS* value: *1.*

Tip

This recipe works with the Simply Filling technique.

Ham and Gherkin Cocktail Kebabs

PREP 10 MIN | **COOK** NONE | **SERVES** 2

4 (1-ounce) slices fat-free low- sodium smoked ham

4 cherry tomatoes, quartered

4 gherkins, each cut into ½-inch pieces

3 tablespoons honey mustard

Roll up each slice of ham and cut crosswise into 4 pieces. On each of 16 cocktail picks or toothpicks, spear 1 piece of ham along with 1 piece of tomato and 1 piece of gherkin. Serve with the honey mustard for dipping.

PER SERVING (8 skewers and 1½ tablespoons honey mustard): 146 Cal, 6 g Fat, 1 g Sat Fat, 0 g Trans Fat, 30 mg Chol, 600 mg Sod, 15 g Carb, 1 g Fib, 10 g Prot, 6 mg Calc. *POINTS* value: *3.*

Open-Face Roast Beef Sandwich Bites

PREP 20 MIN | **COOK** NONE | **SERVES** 4

- **3 tablespoons bottled horseradish, drained**
- **3 tablespoons fat-free mayonnaise**
- **20 slices cocktail (party-style) rye bread, toasted**
- **5 (1-ounce) slices lean deli roast beef, each cut into 4 pieces**
- **10 cherry tomatoes, halved**

1 Stir together the horseradish and mayonnaise in a small bowl. Spread the horseradish mayonnaise evenly over the slices of toast.

2 Place 1 piece of roast beef on each slice of toast. Thread a party toothpick through each tomato half and insert into each sandwich.

PER SERVING (5 sandwiches): 244 Cal, 4 g Fat, 0 g Sat Fat, 0 g Trans Fat, 14 mg Chol, 1,075 mg Sod, 43 g Carb, 6 g Fib, 17 g Prot, 76 mg Calc. *POINTS* value: *4.*

Filling Extra

Place a couple of baby arugula leaves or tender watercress sprigs on the bread before topping with the roast beef.

Turkey and Roasted Pepper Lettuce Wraps

PREP 15 MIN | **COOK** NONE | **SERVES** 8

- **8** **green leaf lettuce leaves**
- **8** **(1-ounce) slices deli roast turkey breast**
- **8** **(¾-ounce) slices Swiss cheese**
- **2** **tablespoons coarse-grain Dijon mustard**
- **1** **(12-ounce) jar roasted red pepper, drained and cut into strips**

1 Lay the lettuce leaves out on a work surface. Layer 1 slice of turkey and 1 slice of Swiss on each lettuce leaf. Spread evenly with the mustard and top evenly with the roasted red pepper.

2 Fold in two opposite sides of a filled lettuce leaf, then roll up to enclose the filling. Secure with a toothpick. Repeat to make a total of 8 rolls.

PER SERVING (1 roll): 137 Cal, 6 g Fat, 4 g Sat Fat, 0 g Trans Fat, 44 mg Chol, 270 mg Sod, 4 g Carb, 1 g Fib, 15 g Prot, 187 mg Calc. *POINTS: 3.*

Pizza Margherita

PREP 10 MIN | **BAKE** 10 MIN | **SERVES** 6

- **1** **(10-ounce) prebaked thin whole-wheat pizza crust**
- **3** **plum tomatoes, thinly sliced**
- **2** **garlic cloves, minced**
- **2** **cups shredded fat-free mozzarella cheese**
- **¼** **cup thinly sliced fresh basil**
- **1** **teaspoon dried oregano**
- **2** **teaspoons olive oil**

1 Preheat the oven to 450°F. Spray a baking sheet with nonstick spray.

2 Place the crust on the prepared baking sheet. Arrange the tomatoes on the crust and sprinkle with the garlic. Top evenly with the mozzarella, basil, and oregano; drizzle with the oil. Bake until the cheese is melted, about 8 minutes. Cut into 6 wedges.

PER SERVING (⅙ of pizza): 198 Cal, 4 g Fat, 1 g Sat Fat, 0 g Trans Fat, 4 mg Chol, 544 mg Sod, 25 g Carb, 4 g Fib, 17 g Prot, 609 mg Calc. *POINTS* value: *3.*

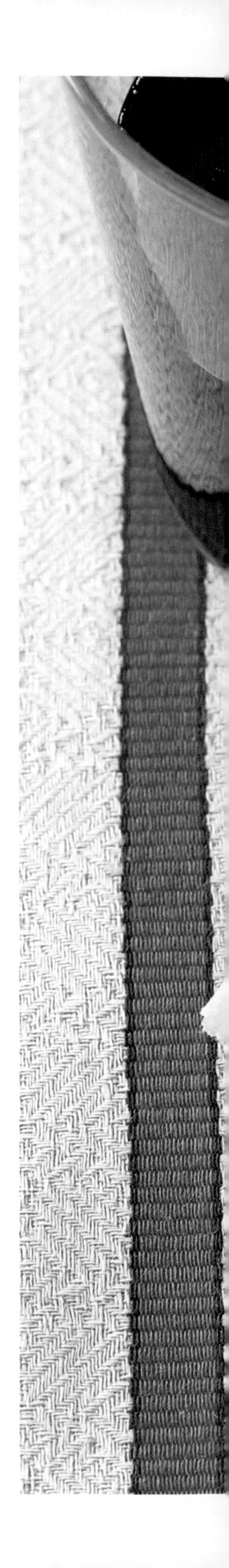

Filling Extra

Add an extra sliced plum tomato and, if you like, top the tomatoes with 1 cup of sliced white or cremini mushrooms.

PIZZA
MARGHERITA

Garlicky Edamame

PREP 10 MIN | **COOK** 5 MIN | **SERVES** 4

1 teaspoon Asian (dark) sesame oil

2 teaspoons minced garlic

1 (10-ounce) bag frozen shelled edamame (green soybeans), thawed

½ teaspoon salt

Pinch cayenne

Heat the oil in a large nonstick skillet over medium-high heat. Add the garlic and cook stirring, until fragrant, about 30 seconds. Stir in the edamame, salt, and cayenne; cook, stirring, until heated through, about 4 minutes.

PER SERVING (¾ cup): 114 Cal, 6 g Fat, 0 Sat Fat, 0 g Trans Fat, 0 Chol, 288 mg Sod, 9 g Carb, 3 g Fiber, 9 g Prot, 105 mg Calc. *POINTS* value: *2.*

In the Kitchen

Edamame, the Japanese word for soybean, grow in clusters on bushy branches. To retain freshness, soybeans are usually parboiled and frozen. Edamame, a rich source of protein, have been enjoyed for over two thousand years in East Asia.

Baked Cheesy Nachos

PREP 10 MIN | **BAKE** 20 MIN | **SERVES** 4

- **36 baked low-fat tortilla chips**
- **1 (15½-ounce) can pinto beans, rinsed and drained**
- **2 tomatoes, chopped**
- **½ small red onion, chopped**
- **1 jalapeño pepper, seeded and minced**
- **1 tablespoon lime juice**
- **½ cup fat-free sour cream**
- **1 cup shredded fat-free Monterey Jack or cheddar cheese**
- **3 tablespoons chopped fresh cilantro**

1 Preheat the oven to 400°F. Spray a 13 x 9-inch baking dish with nonstick spray.

2 Arrange 24 of the tortilla chips in a single layer in the prepared baking dish. Top evenly with the beans, tomatoes, onion, jalapeño pepper, lime juice, and sour cream.

3 Crush the remaining 12 tortilla chips and sprinkle over the sour cream. Top evenly with the Monterey Jack. Bake until heated through and the cheese is melted and bubbling, about 20 minutes. Sprinkle with the cilantro.

PER SERVING (¼ of dish): 266 Cal, 2 Fat, 0 g Sat Fat, 0 g Trans Fat, 6 mg Chol, 514 mg Sod, 36 g Carb, 6 g Fib, 15 g Prot, 500 mg Calc. *POINTS* value: *5.*

recipe index

D

E

M

O

P

Q

R

S

T

V

W

Y

Z

recipes by *POINTS* value

6 POINTS value

7 POINTS value

8 POINTS value

9 POINTS value

dry and liquid measurement equivalents

If you are converting the recipes in this book to metric measurements, use the following chart as a guide.

TEASPOONS	TABLESPOONS	CUPS	FLUID OUNCES
3 teaspoons	1 tablespoon		½ fluid ounce
6 teaspoons	2 tablespoons	⅛ cup	1 fluid ounce
8 teaspoons	2 tablespoons plus 2 teaspoons	⅙ cup	
12 teaspoons	4 tablespoons	¼ cup	2 fluid ounces
15 teaspoons	5 tablespoons	⅓ cup minus 1 teaspoon	
16 teaspoons	5 tablespoons plus 1 teaspoon	⅓ cup	
18 teaspoons	6 tablespoons	¼ cup plus 2 tablespoons	3 fluid ounces
24 teaspoons	8 tablespoons	½ cup	4 fluid ounces
30 teaspoons	10 tablespoons	½ cup plus 2 tablespoons	5 fluid ounces
32 teaspoons	10 tablespoons plus 2 teaspoons	⅔ cup	
36 teaspoons	12 tablespoons	¾ cup	6 fluid ounces
42 teaspoons	14 tablespoons	1 cup minus 2 tablespoons	7 fluid ounces
45 teaspoons	15 tablespoons	1 cup minus 1 tablespoon	
48 teaspoons	16 tablespoons	1 cup	8 fluid ounces

OVEN TEMPERATURE

250°F	120°C	400°F	200°C
275°F	140°C	425°F	220°C
300°F	150°C	450°F	230°C
325°F	160°C	475°F	250°C
350°F	180°C	500°F	260°C
375°F	190°C	525°F	270°C

VOLUME

¼ teaspoon	1 milliliter
½ teaspoon	2 milliliters
1 teaspoon	5 milliliters
1 tablespoon	15 milliliters
2 tablespoons	30 milliliters
3 tablespoons	45 milliliters
¼ cup	60 milliliters
⅓ cup	80 milliliters
½ cup	120 milliliters
⅔ cup	160 milliliters
¾ cup	175 milliliters
1 cup	240 milliliters
1 quart	950 milliliters

LENGTH

1 inch	25 millimeters
1 inch	2.5 centimeters

WEIGHT

1 ounce	30 grams
¼ pound	120 grams
½ pound	240 grams
1 pound	480 grams

Note: Measurement of less than ⅛ teaspoon is considered a dash or a pinch. Metric volume measurements are approximate.